NAMELESS DRUM

SONG WORDS AND OTHER VOICES

Carolyn Hillyer

A comprehensive collection of
one hundred songs and chants

With 48 illustrations

The songs and chants in this book are from
the following CD albums:

Weathered Edge
Cave of Elders
Riven Inside
Old Silverhead
Songs of the Forgotten People
Grandmother Turtle
Heron Valley
House of the Weavers

with additional material from:
*A Circle of Thirteen: Myths and Stories of
Women's Ancient Wisdoms* published 1997
The Oracle of Nights published 2001

All monotone images from original full colour paintings
by Carolyn Hillyer
Front cover painting: Storm the Drummer
Back cover: reindeer skin and birchwood drum made by Carolyn

© Carolyn Hillyer 2004
First edition published 2004 by Seventh Wave Music, England.
Printed and bound in Great Britain.
ISBN Number: 0-9547379-0-3

For a full catalogue of CDs, books and prints
plus list of concerts and exhibitions please contact:
Seventh Wave Music
Lower Merripit Farm, Postbridge,
Dartmoor, Devon, PL20 6TJ England
info@seventhwavemusic.co.uk
www.seventhwavemusic.co.uk

CONTENTS

Most of the songs in this collection have been created over the last thirteen years, a potent number which in itself suggested that this was a good moment to gather together the material of music albums, paintings, books and workshop texts into one cohesive entity. This also represented an opportunity for me to take stock, to review the journey so far, and to clear the decks before embarking on a new phase of work that I was anticipating might carry me into unfamiliar and challenging territory, as well as accompany the maturing of my middle years.

There is, in fact, one song in this book that was written twenty years ago, when my first experience of prolonged and deliberate isolation (in the Nepalese mountains) allowed me at last to uncover my own voice. I probably sang and drummed *Tread Gently* fifty times in my mountain hut before it felt that this first song had truly arrived and it was time to return to the valley. During that same journey, I started to draw, over and again, an image that had inspired me from the dark and oily carvings of an old wooden forest temple. Months later, back in English woods, a second song heralded the approach of my first pregnancy but it was another four years before the many sketches transformed into my first full-size painting of a spirit woman. Then the paintings came quickly, an exhilarating succession of shadowy faces and half-glimpsed forms. Gradually the images were brought into greater focus and my pace slowed. Following my move to Dartmoor's bleak wilderness, the paintings immediately deepened. And, significantly, with these paintings I realised I had now created mouths from which to hear voices. And the voices sang me songs.

It was my partner who, through cunning enticement, sat me in front of a studio microphone for the first time. *House of the Weavers* started as a way of simply catching some of the songs that I was singing as I painted. In fact it marked the beginning of the last thirteen years of composing, recording, performing and sharing my songs and chants. The cycles of painting and song have most often walked hand in hand, one creating the landscape for the other. Sometimes they have been formed independently of each other; *Menopausal Anarchy,* for example, was a straightforward contemplation on life as well as a bid to explore hidden recesses of comedy! The *Weathered Edge* album, the most recent material in this book, was a departure for me in other ways; poised between two long phases of painting, one completed and the other waiting to arrive, I realised with some surprise that the only image I had that could truly reflect the feeling of this CD was my own face – carrying, as it does for each of us, the lines and markings carved into the skin that describe life and how it has been lived so far.

Memories are placed into the land by the people who have travelled across it, or dwelt there for some time. These memories are held deep within the stone belly of the earth, and survive any amount of surface chaos or neglect. They are the rich source of our inspiration and awakening, feeding our search and guiding our tracks. They also fertilise our myths and stories, revealing the ancient patterns, maps and symbols that might serve us on our journeys. From this place emerged the Nameless Drum, so called because it was new; unnamed because there was no one there to give it one, or to hear its voice. The Nameless Drum was born out of the empty land bringing with it song and rhythm. We, the people, came to hear it, to name it and to claim it, to draw it into our stories and our consciousness. The Nameless Drum describes the voice of our first and oldest communication with the spirits of the land.

These writings may be used alongside the recorded CDs so that the music remains an integral part of the songs and chants. Or they may be read independently of melody and rhythm, the words alone thus taking the form of ritual poetry. Some of the more simply constructed chants become fully alive when sung by many harmonizing voices. In this context the chant takes on a character of its own, created anew by each group of singers. I was awed by the experience of listening to seventy women sing The Sisterhood of Weavers inside a stone roundhouse, the many layers of their voices coiling up inside the high thatched roof cone.

Many of these songs may be used or adapted for ceremonial circles or rites of passage. Others may be best experienced when whispered quietly in the dawn or to a silent moon. Songs can be flighty creatures, diving across the land like summer birds or sweeping down through icy rivers, but the sacred land releases songs to all of us. And as we remember how to honour and celebrate with voice and drum, we will find that we are running a swift road towards our own songs.

I did not find my voice to sing until I found songs that had meaning for me. I did not hear the deeper rhythms of my life until I began to sound them on my drum. Anyone of us can sing and drum once we have been moved by the spirit of something; this is the most ancient gift that connects us to this land, to an awareness of sacred earth and to our oldest ancestors. It also creates bonds between ourselves and others by strengthening our clan spirit. We can dance and sing and pray a thousand ways.

ANCESTOR SONG

Weathered Edge

When the land is still
Even shadows pause
When the moon is cast
Through an open door
We are calling you
We are calling you.

Find this place familiar, do you
Find this place familiar?
Now the night is opening to us
Now the night is bringing,
The night is bringing you.

When a veil is spun
Far across the reeds
When a silence builds
Below the waiting trees
We are calling you
We are calling you.

Feel our skin is touching, do you
Feel our skin is touching?
Now our bones are singing gently
Now our bones remember,
Our bones remember you.

When a clear flute weeps
Beside the river's chill
When a dark drum beats
Upon an empty hill
We are calling you
We are calling you.

See our hands entwining, do you
See our faces merging?
Now our souls are overlapping
And this place is blessed,
This place is blessed by you.

When the land is still
Even shadows pause
When the moon is cast
Through an open door
We are calling you
We are calling you
We are calling you
We are calling you.

AUTUMN BLESSING

Riven Inside

How may we dance the Autumn Dance?
When there's a reckless wind beneath our arms
Storm-swept and tying madness into our hair
Then we will know how we may dance.

How may we sing the Autumn Song?
When every breath reveals a silent prayer
Echoes that rise and tremble within our lips
Then we will know how we may sing.

How may we pray the Autumn Prayer?
When the full-bellied fruits of thought and dream
Are gathered ready for the journey in
Then we will know how we may pray.

How may we dance the Autumn Dance?
When there's a reckless wind beneath our arms
Storm-swept and tying madness into our hair
Then we will know how we may dance
Then we will know how we may dance.

The Oracle was very old
by the time we found her in the
half light of the half moon, under
skies that stretched above us like a
vast black vaulted roof;
though we gathered at the table
of her wise abundant visions,
eager with the questions that we
sought to match with answers,
we soon realised as we waited she had none,
and she turned her head towards us,
half in light and half in shadow,
half in quick-winged youth, the other
twisted by the ravages of age,
and her eyes were white and empty
and her forehead glowed and glimmered
with the tracings of a chart,
a map of hidden treasure,
that turned and spun upon its axis,
thus she spoke,
to see or speak a future or
a truth, or make a vision is
the gift of each and all,
there is only one answer
to each and every question
which is to open trusting wings and fly inside,
then the ground gave way beneath us
and we leapt into the black air
and we flew into the secrets of the night,
and we flew into the secrets of the night.

BERRIDRAUN

Songs of the Forgotten People

A traveller through the winter lands was lost amid the mire
He saw a figure wander there and followed it a while
But when he reached the higher ground the figure she was gone
For he had seen the Berridraun a-stepping out alone.

You'll never catch a sight of her when spring is in the land
She scorns the dance of summer and the Greening's gentle hand
But when the autumn chill has got the earth within its jaw
The Berridraun again will be a-walking on the moor.

When winds have claimed the forest and the broken trees do fall
The ice is cracking sharply on each captured granite wall
And boulders in the torrent roll and crash beneath the foam
It is the sound of Berri's bones a-shaking up a storm.

Her feet pass on the muddy trail but they leave not a mark
She casts no shadow when the moon at full pierces the dark
She slips between the misted veils that hang beyond the stones
And goes where few may journey save the ancient Berridraun.

So the night it presses close and its edge is raw
Do you hear the soulful keening that spreads out across the
    moor?
It haunts our restless sleeping and entwines our memory
It is the cry of Berridraun a-travelling through our dreams.

Let us go down to where time and the rocky water spills
And we may see the Berridraun a-coming by the hill.

Riven Inside

Be wary of lovers who come from the greenwood
Dissolved in the light of a full summer bloom
They may draw you like deer to the glade and the spinney
Held fast by the charm of their glittering tunes

Take heed of sweet bells and the silver bright whistles
Voices that rise and so beautifully blend
Though the dance is a whirl of fine footstep and frenzy
A faerie-led song never reaches the end

You may leap for the moon like a hare on the mountain
You may shout for the wind like a rook in a tree
The excitement you feel is a mist and a fancy
A shimmering glimmering love-memory

The Myth Hunter drifts in a hollow enchantment
The True Bride is plucking at nettles and dew
The dance is compelling and time an illusion
Keep pace with the music whatever you do

Thin fingers are pinching from thorn bush and briar
The haunts of the elvish are slipping away
The dancers are tripping back into the shadows
Wish not for a greening wood lover to stay

BLACK CORAL FISHMOTHER

Grandmother Turtle

Fishmothers are crowing as we
squat below the wooden boats and
spit and smoke the evening and our
jabbing tongues are leaping through the
silver fish blood shallows as we
cast the eye and read the black sand.

Black coral skull woman
Thin lizard track woman
Volcanic sand woman
Fishwater hand woman
Sharp wooden eye woman
Soul catching gate woman
Loud mocking ghost woman
Big laughing death woman

Wash the children in the grey stream
chase the old men from their bottles
gut the catch and sing for plenty
coax and cook the midnight stories
guard the blink of fishboat lanterns
on the dark and oily water.

Black coral skull woman
Thin lizard track woman
Volcanic sand woman
Fishwater hand woman
Sharp wooden eye woman
Soul catching gate woman
Loud mocking ghost woman
Big laughing death woman

Midwives to the dying
pass beneath the crumbling archway
of the temple and we reach beyond
the purple gate and pull the
new ones through into the red dawn
and the boats return at first light

Black coral skull woman
Thin lizard track woman
Volcanic sand woman
Fishwater hand woman
Sharp wooden eye woman
Soul catching gate woman
Loud mocking ghost woman
Big laughing death woman

BLESSED BE THE BLOOD

Old Silverhead

This chant is created by the interweaving harmonies of many voices. It is
sung to honour our good blood, our ancient blood, the blood of joy and
sorrow, the deep symbol of our shared experience as women.

Blessed be the blood on your skirt
Blessed be the blood on your thighs
Blessed be the blood
Blessed be the blood

Red moon red moon
Red moon red moon
Blessed be the blood
Blessed be the blood

Red moon pulling woman
Red moon filling woman
Blessed be the blood
Blessed be the blood

Moon pulling woman
Moon filling woman
Blessed be the blood
Blessed be the blood

BLOODFLOWER

Old Silverhead

Bloodflower describes a girl who has entered her first bleeding. In this song she approaches the circle to be admitted as a new woman. Symbolically she breaks the first tie between daughter and mother, as she moves towards her greater independence. (See also *Following First Blood* page 43)

Maad'n doi   maad'n doi   la-hyo
Maad'n doi   maad'n doi   la-hyo he ēd'n
(Translation: mother with daughter closely bound until blood)

I am travelling in moon waters
I am flowing in moon waters
I am growing in moon waters
new woman in moon waters

standing at holy doors
open up open up
and I shall enter
standing at holy doors
open up open up
and I shall enter

honour to my mother's blood
honour to my sister's blood
honour to my own blood
honour to my mother's blood
honour to my sister's blood
honour to my own blood

BONE HILL HAG

Grandmother Turtle

Additional words from: A Circle of Thirteen

Black moon
Earth tomb
Deep stone
Carved bone

We are gathered here at dark of thirteenth moon.
All light is pulled down far into earth's womb.
Above the night rises the dome of holy Bone Hill.
Silence fills ancient place and this circle waits.
Circle waits, fire is lit, circle moves, slowly turns.
Slowly rolls around the flame as the dance begins.
Women's feet on the soil, women's hands form the ring
Women's voices murmur low, women's bodies slow, slow.
Chants softly dip and rise, fire held in women's eyes.
Now circle gathers pace, gently as the power grows.
Round the flames women step, stamp with the rising beat.
Here are our mysteries locked within this spinning wheel.
Here are our secret lives, here are our greatest truths.
Strongly spun and stronger still as the circle turns.

Above the brow of Bone Hill, golden sparks hit the sky.
Opposite and unseen, another fire is burning there.
Men's feet, men's song, build their mystery ring.

Grey eyes
Moon wise
Dark stag
Silver hag

Circle spins within its trance, dissolves into the dance.
Waves of many layered song swell and wash around the ring.
Now the power reaching out, now the moment judged complete.
Away from circle and from fire, a single shaded figure steps.
Silver headed Hag makes steady course towards the Hill,
Where the protecting veil yields to her hidden code.
Carved tracery in stone, entrance to the sacred tomb.
Timeless curve, ancient route, narrow pass beneath earth's skin.
Silver Hag within the hill, rising through the granite coil.
Fingers follow guiding rock, shadows slip from flaming torch.

As the hag moves so the Stag, spiral within spiral curls,
Travelling from another fire, different circle, different song.
He enters by another key, his tunnel turning separately.
Track they inwards, ever deep, down towards heart of Bone Hill.

Good words
Well met
Old pact
Newly set

Hag arrives at inner place, as she comes so comes the Stag,
Each from narrow spiral born into the centre of the Hill,
Each the other facing as they take position in the cave.
Dark stone womb wherein stands the great Bone Hill Drum.
Silent waiting watching pair, both lit by fiery brand,
And their shadows mixing high across the rocky dome.
Greeting offered and received, words so special, so revered,
Words that find an opening, make a gate and hold it wide,
Words that meet and absorb, fusing time and blending souls,
Words along which magic moves,
Where threads of common bond are cast.
Thus the ancient promise is being given between Hag and Stag.

Witness
Silent land
Gifts from
Ancient hand

So speaks the Hag: I carry here much
Of deed and feeling, thought and dream.
New songs are only shaped from older voices,
Dances freshly formed from remembered steps long gone.
This circle is vast and we but one turn of it.
Take this, Old Brother, it is a thing
No more than itself, no less than everything.
Here is love far greater than expected
And grief more healing than we could have known.
Strangely different, hugely distant,
Hands will touch across the raw.
Hate is dissolved in the water offered to the burned.

So speaks the Stag: I carry here a tiny seed
On which the whole is rocked from side to side.
What has preceded teaches simply that
Balance is the key that constantly eludes.
While outer reaches swing beyond control,
This pivot rests, perfectly still.
Take this, Old Sister, it is the only gift
That can make sense, the centre pin.
Here is compassion so full it spills the edges,
And sadnesses expanded into many joys.
Fiercely separate, darkly opposite,
Hearts will love across the gap.
As the burned accepts the water, so is the firekeeper freed.

Strikes twice
Stag horn
On Bone
Hill Drum

Exchange the gifts and it is done, again the pact is sealed tight.
By the mound the circles spin, hear the double call resound.
Horn of stag and hide of doe twice united at the Drum.
Twice pronounce that what is made will be torn apart by none.
As the stag, as the doe, draw breath from the greenwood soil,
So this sacred vow takes life within the Bone Hill Drum.

Two valleys
One ridge
Two spirals
One bridge

I am the ridge, declares the Stag,
Where two strands are running separately,
I am the place from where to see the whole.
From these eyes see winding valleys unknowingly embrace.
From these eyes see how their distant destinies are joined.
I am the witness to all this.
I am the wider view.

I am the bridge, replies the Hag,
I hold the arm of each.
I am the linking of the chain,
Through me the circle is complete.
Inner connected to the outer, dark is touching light.
Opposites may reach across me,
I am the glass wherein two reflections meet.

Bone Hill
Drum sings
Stag and Hag
Link rings

Ceremony brought to end, two circles turning still,
Two dances melted into one, two songs that found a harmony.
Silver Hag begins her slow outward spiral of return.
Stag has also set his foot towards the early morning air.
They walk with newer understanding, wiser insight, greater peace,
Carry these to feed the circles of women and men.
This is a precious union, alliance both fragile and strong,
Two mystery rings forever rolling, do not in isolation spin.
All one does effects the other, because of each the other learns,
Joined by the spiral thread that passes through the Bone Hill Drum.

Old Silverhead

Spin woman spin
turn woman turn
twist the strands onto your spindle
braid them as one

Spin woman spin
turn woman turn
wind the yarn around your fingers
keep your focus strong

Enlaced with your purpose and
entwined with your power
gather your threads before
you set your good work down
woman spin

Spin woman spin
turn woman turn
curl the clay within your hands
give form to the bowl

Spin woman spin
turn woman turn
shape the wet pot firmly because
balance is all

Smoothed by your purpose and
fired by your power
burnish the sides before
you set your good work down
woman spin

BROWN BIRDS TURNING

Grandmother Turtle

We sing of your deep heart
We sing of your sweet pain
We sing of your sad eye
Brown Birds Turning, Brown Birds Turning

We drink of your bright tear
We pray by your bowed head
We cradle you at your breaking
Brown Birds Turning, Brown Birds Turning

Your sorrow is a cold sky
Your grieving is a dark hill
Your weeping is a grey mist
Brown Birds Turning, Brown Birds Turning

There's beauty in the cold sky
There's courage on the dark hill
There's truth within the grey mist
Brown Birds Turning, Brown Birds Turning

The river once ran shallow
The forest once a waste land
It takes time to birth a mountain
Brown Birds Turning, Brown Birds Turning

We sing of your deep heart
We sing of your sweet pain
We sing of your sad eye
We sing of your sad eye…

CELEBRATION ROAD

Heron Valley

The people saw that the song had been broken, yet there was none who knew of a way to bring the pieces together. And so they journeyed out through the fabric of many lives and walked at the edges of many worlds. They carried their children on their backs and to the breast of each was held a small bundle containing a fragment of the song that had once been whole.

Their naked feet moved swiftly and strongly over the land and their bodies swung with the rhythms of the earth. The limbs of their sons were filled with the fires of the desert and the bellies of their daughters were rocked by the tides of the moon.

At last they came to the place where the spiral turns, the hearth of the Three Spirit Women. And the people squatted low onto the soil and from their bundles drew forth the broken pieces of their song. And even as the Women plucked up the fragments and sent them hurling up into the air, the people saw that which had been split apart became whole once more. So the song of the people was restored to them and their voices rode out on the southern winds.

Someone is running at the edge of the world
Strong bare desert feet
Someone is drumming at the dawning of the earth
Swift steps mark the beat
Something is carried here close to the heart
So small so light
Somewhere a universe is starting to turn
Huge raw brave and bright

A song is opening and touching the sky
The rhythm is true and the vision is bold
Dancing the dream and living the joy
Spirit is walking a celebration road
Spirit is rising
Spirit is moving
Spirit is walking a celebration road…

CLOUD

Weathered Edge paintings

She is CLOUD the Visioner
who holds the unfolding story
as drifting thoughts
fanned by her wing
made of a thousand eyes.
She is constantly elusive
and yet somehow constant.
Her dance is a dream,
a finely beaded pattern of
promise and desire.
She dances where
subtle form is
created momentarily,
drawn in by
rings of stone
or ever-changing whim
or this dragonfly
that skits through the
first evening perfumes of
MIDSUMMER.

COME INTO OUR DREAM

Old Silverhead

This is a welcome song, given to us by our ancient mothers when we are
brought to the rim of the circle to meet for the first time the community of
women into which we have been born.

You are born to the many and born to the one
In the lap of your mother you are held by us all
Come into our dream, come into our dream
Come into our dream, now it's yours

Can you feel our protection as we bind you a spell?
Do you hear our blessing you beautiful child?
Come into our dream, come into our dream
Come into our dream, now it's yours

There's a coil of all women encircling time
We are dancing through mirrors, an unbroken line
Come into our dream, come into our dream
Come into our dream, now it's yours

From mother to daughter to daughter to babe
At the breast of one woman you are fed by us all
Come into our dream, come into our dream
Come into our dream, now it's yours

To the earth house of life you have quietly returned
We greet you with honour and welcome you in
Come into our dream, come into our dream
Come into our dream, now it's yours

CROW

The Oracle of Nights

We came into the darkness
of the mortuary house
through the narrow blackened doorway
where the souls of dead and dying
clustered, plucking at the living
as we passed into the cold house,
the stinking mortuary house,
and we sat among the bones
and all the casings of the body,
hair and nail and tooth and gristle,
claw and fur and skin and beak,
and many, many bones
piled up into the corners
of the mortuary house,
and we stayed below the shadows
and we slowly sucked the memory
held within each tiny fragment,
we devoured the soft bone marrow
and licked clean each head and toe bone
we were rocking back and forwards
singing gently to the ghosts
that we absorbed into our bodies,
that we took into our bellies,
where the memories fermented,
rose and bubbled in our bellies,
like a rich wine of the dead,
like a rich wine of the dead.

Weathered Edge

I will be the hunter
Of the fires that burn cold
Flames that fuel the quickening
Of the unborn earth
I will be the hunter
I will hunt the cold fire
Cruelty of diamonds
And the truth of bones

Hoy yoy yoy yoy yoy yoy yoy!

I will track a new prey
My course is uncertain
I'm compelled to hunt you
I must stalk answers
You have led me far off
Where the great hills mock me
Cruelty of diamonds
And the truth of bones

Hoy yoy yoy yoy yoy yoy yoy!

I am strong in spirit
Hunter without mercy
I'm a million fragments
Held by light alone
I become an arrow
I become a quick spear
Cruelty of diamonds
And the truth of bones

Hoy yoy yoy yoy yoy yoy yoy!

You have marked me deeply
Each bone in my body
You have scratched and carved me
Darkly shaping me
Beautiful and fearsome
Symbols that hide secrets
Cruelty of diamonds
And the truth of bones

Hoy yoy yoy yoy yoy yoy yoy!

They say an icy landscape
Carries no illusions
Everything is peeled back
Naked in the air
Now I understand
What to be alive means
Cruelty of diamonds
And the truth of bones

Hoy yoy yoy yoy yoy yoy yoy!

Circling and advancing
Through the hunting dance while
This our painful contract
Glitters like a wound.
I dream one day I'll hunt
Released from frozen forests
Free from cruel diamonds
And the truth of bones

Hoy yoy yoy yoy yoy yoy yoy!

I will be the hunter
I am strong in spirit
I become the arrow
I become the spear
Now I understand
What to be alive means
Cruelty of diamonds
And the truth of bones

Hoy yoy yoy yoy yoy yoy yoy!
Hoy yoy yoy yoy yoy yoy yoy!

EARTHCRONE

Old Silverhead

Earthcrone has experienced her final bleeding and her womb now begins to build up and retain the magic of the monthly blood flow. This chant honours her entry into the crone stage of her life, as she dedicates herself to the earth. This is a stamping song. Each chorus ends with a great shout: GA! to emphasise the power of her actions.

BEL HOY SEE'CH GA!
(blood now held inside)
MA HOY LUN GA!
(power now flows inside)

Crow comes to where Oak is slowly
bleeding, in her claws a thin thread

BEL HOY SEE'CH GA!
MA HOY LUN GA!

Crow says this is the last I bring
and the Oak is spilling red tears

BEL HOY SEE'CH GA!
MA HOY LUN GA!

Crow she smells of a wet cave, a
bruised bundle of warm southern herbs

BEL HOY SEE'CH GA!
MA HOY LUN GA!

The last thread drops onto the moss
and brown of winter then it fades

BEL HOY SEE'CH GA!
MA HOY LUN GA!

Oak feels the quickened pulse, the
power builds inside her crusted skin

BEL HOY SEE'CH GA!
MA HOY LUN GA!

A Crow sits on an Oak, Oak
is silent, they listen to earth

BEL HOY SEE'CH GA!
MA HOY LUN GA!

Crow and Oak together they sit, they
are silent, they listen to earth

BEL HOY SEE'CH GA!
MA HOY LUN GA!

EGYPT DUST

House of the Weavers

I knocked at the door of the Three Guardians
and I beseeched them:
give me wings again O Mothers.
There is one who sends
and one who waits to receive.
I am a messenger who moves between horizons.
Give me flight O Mothers.

We fly, we fly
our gentle wings this heart enfold
We carry, we carry
a precious song to you our sister
We feel, we feel
the winter of your sad waiting
We call, we call
know you that we are near now
We seek, we seek
we send out light into the shadows
We trust, we trust
the dawn will bring us to you.

Wide eagle mountain passes
Deep plunging misty valleys
Red blood baked rock
Hot dust hazy desert
Silent watching night forest
Thin silver serpent trails.

We find, we find
we call into your dreaming
We circle, we circle
spiral into your waking soul
We touch, we touch
the wings of all the birds embrace you
We lift, we lift
you up into your mountain vision
We dance, we dance
in the wise glow of your shining
We love, we love
the beauty of your rising

Swiftly coming swiftly coming
Softly coming softly coming
Sweet Egypt dust in your hair
Warm musk lingers on your skin
Soft waves of your whispering
I hear, I fly
I carry your timeless love
and follow footsteps
across the burning sand.

EIGHT BEADS CHANT

Old Silverhead

This chant is formed around the names of eight stages of womanhood, which are symbolized by eight beads or amulets, collected throughout the course of a woman's life and worn on a cord around the neck. For GIRLSEED, a smooth hard seed; for BLOODFLOWER, a piece of red mountain coral; for FRUITMOTHER, a cowrie shell; for SPINMOTHER, a spiral made from copper; for MIDWOMAN, amber; for EARTHCRONE, a bead carved from oak or other forest wood; for STONECRONE, a rounded river pebble; and for BONE, a slice of bone left on the land by a wild creature. OLD SILVERHEAD, who is the oldest woman, wears the eight beads here on behalf of us all, as she guides us through to our own time as elder women.

Girlseed
Bloodflower
Fruitmother
Spinmother
Midwoman
Earthcrone
Stonecrone
Bone

Heron Valley

A song for the last weeks of pregnancy. Written for my daughter.

We float in a water with no shore
Moon child, womb child
We slide across a landscape with no horizon
Moon child, womb child
I am filled by you
I am filled by you.

We are held in a stillness between two sighs
Moon child, womb child
We live in the silence of a song with no words
Moon child, womb child
I am filled by you
I am filled by you.

This is our shared time
This is our shared time
I wait for the ripe time
You are waiting too.

FIRE PIT SINGING

Grandmother Turtle

There's a woman at the river
and she is called Fire Pit Singing
and she's leaping through the jungle
and she roams the steamy forest
and her skin is hot and glistens
and she's crouching by the water
and she's digging in the coarse sand
and she gathers river pebbles
and she nests them in the fire pit
and she sets the small fire burning
and the flames are licking lightly
and she bakes the river pebbles
and she cracks the hot stones open
and she tastes the molten centre
and she drinks the burning liquid
and it pours like tongues of amber
and she's swallowing the fire song
and it pours like tongues of amber
and she's swallowing the fire song
and she's crouched above the fire pit
and the song is diving deeply
and it grows within her belly
and she curls up in the ashes
of the fire pit by the river.

There's a big cat at the river
and she's sliding through the jungle
and her muscles tense and ripple
and her claws flick in the pale light
and her wild cat eyes are flashing
and she moves within a spring coiled
and she moves within a spring coiled
and she's pausing at the sand hole
and she watches Fire Pit Singing
and she's waiting by the ashes
and she waits within a spring coiled
and her wild cat eyes are flashing
and her wild cat eyes are flashing.

Fire Pit Woman now is rising
and she grasps the jungle body
and she's whirling through the forest
and she growls and roars and rages
and her throat is opened darkly
and her voice is flying wildly
and she's singing out the fire songs
and she sings within a vast fire
and she's singing out the fire songs
and she's birthed a mighty passion
and the cat is leaping with her
and she sings with Fire Pit Woman
and their bodies leap together
and they sing the heat of anger

and they sing the flames of great joy
and they sing about a fierce love
and they sing about a strong life
and the fire songs fill the jungle
and they spill beyond the forest
and they ride the stormy weather
and they move out into the wide world
where they light the fires of many
where they light the fires of many.

FOLLOWING FIRST BLOOD

Grandmother Turtle

Additional words: A Circle of Thirteen

This song is offered to young women when they first arrive at womanhood with the onset of bleeding. The text is the voice of the guardian of this journey, who traditionally trains and prepares them for this rite, and finally accompanies them to the door of the women's house.

From the hearth of this House flows our good blood,
our birth blood and our death blood.
From the fire of this hearth springs the life of our bellies
and the light of our souls.
To the centre of this fire we are running true and leaping clear.
We are bound like swift arrows to the heart of our Mother.

I am greeting you, ancient and many bloodsisters of the motherhouse, who have gathered here throughout the spiral of time. I am greeting you, beloved daughters of the Bloodflower, who squat here on the dark soil of this blessed place. I am greeting you, long-legged foals of the mighty Wind Horse, arrived at last and newly entered into this circle of wisdom.

You have braided your hair as hunters. As young women you have claimed yourselves. You have fashioned a bow from your supple spirit and carved arrows from your fierce intent. I have seen your limbs grow strong like young pine and your minds sharpen to the crystal clarity of a winter lake. I have witnessed your joyous adventure.

I have run beside you as you raced the great Mare, your lean bodies pulling fast away from childish concerns. I have been the sharp blade along which to test yourselves, the taut bow string against which to push. I have been the dark place to fear and in which to overcome fear. We have hunted well together, you and I, and your race was good. You ran beyond your self-doubt and your need. You embraced the forest, running barefoot to the drum and singing out the name of your cherished prey. You covered great distances and ever-shifting terrains. Your bodies merged into the rhythm of the chase. You ran straight into your power. Now go to your mother and greet her as a bloodsister. She who now mourns the small girl lost to her shall celebrate the woman-daughter who returns.

May you honour your Bloodflower and walk proud
May you honour the Thirteen Moonmothers and grow wise
May you honour the bloodsisters of this House and give truth
May you honour yourself and be complete.

Comes the barefoot runner
She raises her warrior bow
Daughter of the fast drum
Fly pure eye of her intent!
Runs beside the Wind Horse
Far into the virgin pine
She is stalking bloodflower
How she hunts the Women's House!
She is following first blood
Heyiya ha makakēshé

Makakēshé wakiva momo
heyiya ha makakēshé
sasutdēyo beꞔhnini Ooma
laklak gavo beꞔhnini Ooma
maka nechi ragelé rhuya
wakiva i amam i rhuya

We the barefoot runners
Raising high our warrior bows
Daughters of the fast drum
Fly pure eye of our intent!
We run beside the Wind Horse
Far into the virgin pine
We are stalking bloodflower
How we hunt the Women's House!
We are following first blood
Heyiya ha makakēshé

Makakēshé wakiva momo
heyiya ha makakēshé
sasutdēyo beꞔhnini Ooma
laklak gavo beꞔhnini Ooma
maka nechi ragelé rhuya
wakiva i amam i rhuya

FRUITMOTHER

Old Silverhead

Fruitmother describes a woman at a point in her life where she is entering into her full creative potential and starting to establish the direction that she wishes her life to take. This song honours the road that she has chosen and acknowledges her emerging power.

Here is my road
I have chosen it
It delights me
It pulls me on.

Here is my voice
I am finding it
I am running now
Towards my song.

Here are my hands
They are moving fast
There are many worlds
They can create.

Here is my courage
I drink deeply
I leap and climb
Beyond my fear.

Here is my road, I am birthing spirit
Here is my voice, I am birthing spirit
Here are my hands, I am birthing spirit
Here is my courage, I am birthing spirit

Here are my prayers
I plant a garden for
My dreams to grow
This soil is good.

Here is my heart
I am holding love
Delicious love
It hurts my breast.

Here is my circle
I can go anywhere
And still I'm here
Within its arms.

Here is my womb
New life, new life
My belly's strong
I am the Fruit.

Here are my prayers, I am birthing spirit
Here is my heart, I am birthing spirit
Here is my circle, I am birthing spirit
Here is my womb, I am birthing spirit
Here is my road, I am birthing spirit
Here is my road, I am birthing spirit

GIRLSEED

Old Silverhead

So I left the warm fields of my own maidenhood,
and I followed the course of my restless years.
I came to the place where my mothering stood
and this is the daughter that I found here.

She's the raw and the rhythm of all that I feel,
the promise of grace newly born.
She's the mystery of love in its wild poetry,
my mirror and I am her door,
she's my mirror and I am her door.

I said how can I dare to invite you along
on a journey of which I'm unsure?
And how can I hope that I'll learn to be strong
for my own life as well as for yours?

She's the raw and the rhythm of all that I feel,
the promise of grace newly born.
She's the mystery of love in its wild poetry,
my mirror and I am her door,
she's my mirror and I am her door.

Fear fled from my breast when I looked in her eyes
for the trust that I saw gave courage to me.
She reached for my hand as she came to my side
and these are the words that she sung to me:

You're the raw and the rhythm of all that I feel,
the promise of grace newly born.
You're the mystery of love in its wild poetry,
my mirror and I am your door,
you're my mirror and I am your door.

GIVE ME WILD

Heron Valley

Storm beast rides in the belly of the night
Give me wild give me wild
Give me wild give me wild

Storm beast curled on the wing of the wind
Give me wild give me wild
Give me wild give me wild

Waters amber waters crashing waters stinging rains
Wash me through wash me through
Give me wild give me wild

Mist yawning mist spinning mist trailing spirits
Wrap me round wrap me round
Give me wild give me wild

Rock dripping rock cutting rock broken warriors
Hold me strong hold me strong
Give me wild give me wild

Clouds rolling clouds darkness clouds heavy thunder
Press me close press me close
Give me wild give me wild

Earth twisting earth heaving earth swaying belly
Rock me hard rock me hard
Give me wild give me wild

Light flashing light piercing light bolting horses
Fire my soul fire my soul
Give me wild give me wild

Trees beating trees madness trees leaping shadows
Free my dance free my dance
Give me wild give me wild

Storm beast rides in the belly of the night
Give me wild give me wild
Give me wild give me wild

Storm beast curled on the wing of the wind
Give me wild give me wild
Give me wild give me wild

GOOD MOTHER HONEY

Grandmother Turtle

Good Mother Honey, Good Mother Honey
We shall eat from your wild berry pie
Good Mother Honey, Good Mother Honey
We shall drink from your sweet dripping wells
Good Mother Honey, Good Mother Honey
And the rain comes gently to bless your rich soil
Rain singing…

Good Mother Honey, Good Mother Honey
So plays the hymn of the fruit and the seed
Good Mother Honey, Good Mother Honey
So turns the dance of the herb and the hive
Good Mother Honey, Good Mother Honey
And the sun steps lightly to clothe your warm skin
Sun murmurs…

Good Mother Honey, Good Mother Honey
We weave through your orchards, we sway through your fields
Good Mother Honey, Good Mother Honey
We coil round your pastures, we circle your pools
Good Mother Honey, Good Mother Honey
And the air spins softly to tangle your hair
Breeze sighing…

Good Mother Honey, Good Mother Honey
Here's praise to the creamy gold breasts of your land
Good Mother Honey, Good Mother Honey
Here's joy in the harvest of your deep garden
Good Mother Honey, Good Mother Honey
And the soil gives plenty to feed your life dance
Earth whispers…

Good Mother Honey we shall eat from you
Good Mother Honey we shall drink of you
Good Mother Honey we shall dance with you
Good Mother Honey we shall live by you

Southernwood, apple mint,
tarragon, lavender,
feverfew, aconite,
comfrey, caraway,
hyssop, wood betony,
balm of gilead,
borage, wild peppermint,
pennyroyal, purple sage,
rosemary, camomile,
ginger mint, lemon balm,
thyme, winter savoury,
tansy, marigold,
nettle, wormwood,
golden marjoram,
southernwood, apple mint,
tarragon, lavender
we shall dance…
dance with you…

GRANDMOTHER TURTLE

Grandmother Turtle

Additional words: A Circle of Thirteen

And we came at night from the belly of the sea
and we hung our braids on a lone tree
and we held our secret through an empty age
we hid our knowing in a simple jar of clay

and we sound our rattles
and we beat our drums
we're moving slow
on the cold sand…

And we walked on shards and we swam through flame
we dared to bleed and we dared to burn
and our fragments lay on the deep forest floor
in a clearing where our voices drift and call

and we sound our rattles
and we beat our drums
we're moving slow
on the cold sand…

And the face of the rock was pitted and scarred
the people cried when their dying was hard
but we watched it all through ancient eyes
and the circle held as the Turtle Waters did rise

and we sound our rattles
and we beat our drums
we're moving slow
on the cold sand...

And we cast our daughters to the flying winds
and we gave them up to the crashing waves
and they sailed in their boats to a distant shore
and they hung their braids as we had done before

and we sound our rattles
and we beat our drums
we're moving slow
on the cold sand...

The forest opens up,
opens up to receive us
and we walk for the first time
in the joy of a wild place.
And our toes are in the roots
and our arms are in the branches
and we come to the forest place
with earth smeared on our cheeks.

Beneath the damp earth bower
of the Old Turtle Mother
we sit in the half-light.
The Turtle she is silent,
she lies still and silent,

on her low wooden pallet,
her face never moving
but for black eyes blinking slowly
in the dim light as she listens
and she watches.
She has sat here for a long time
sat with her clay pot,
waiting and watching
for a hundred hundred years.

And in the trees above us
hang the braids of the Old Ones,
many hair braids are hanging,
given by the women
who have come to this forest,
who have sat with the clay pot.
Many hair braids are hanging
as a curtain about us
and they move in the soft breeze,
they are swaying in the breeze.
And from a tree before us
hang the braids of the First Ones,
thirteen ancient braids,
white and bound in rotted rags.
They have hung on this tree
since before there was a forest,
hung on a lone tree
when the First Ones arrived.
We sit with the Turtle
and we sit and we listen,
we watch in the half-light
of the deep forest bower.

We rise and we walk
out into the clear dawn.
In the darkness we've drunk deeply
from the words of the clay pot.
On the mud floor we have pieced
the broken shards together,
leaned our heads to the mouth
of the jar, and we have heard
a thousand thousand whispered prayers.

This is our vessel,
our beautiful clay pot,
our mystery, our memory,
our wisdom and our song.

Carrying our clay pot
we move slowly from the forest.
We drum to the fires
and we rattle to the ocean.
We sing to the changes,
the ever-dancing changes,
and we sing to the things
that remain the same.
We walk through the charred
pieces of the endings,
we walk through the seeds
of what now begins.
We walk through the ashes
washed by the waters,
our feet mark a trail
now the sand is cold…

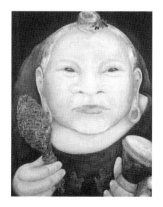

GRANDMOTHER WEAVES-THE-WIND

Grandmother Turtle

This piece appears at the end of the Grandmother Turtle album and features fragments of the songs for each of the thirteen grandmothers described there. Thus a complex weaving of melodies and patterns is formed around the shuttle rhythm of the chant. This song represents the sound of the grandmothers working at the great bowl-shaped loom of life within the primordial and timeless House of Weavers.

She's coming. She's coming. Quick, quick, hurry up! She has come.
What is this place? What is this place?
What do you want, girl? What do you want? What do you want, girl?
What is this place?
This is no place. No place. No place. You know that nothing is as it seems.
But there's nothing here.
Precisely! Ha! Precisely! A witch who's kind saves time.
But where do I keep it?
In my pocket of course! Want a nice piece of time, girl?
I have no time. I'm out of time.
It takes time. It takes time. Give it to me.
What? What do I give you?
Your madness. Will you bring to me your madness child?
But I need it. I need it.
Then I sweep, sweep, sweep you out of the door.
Push her.
But I don't know how to fly.
You don't need wings. Use your memory. Use your memory. And so we cast our daughters to the flying winds. You are weaving your own footsteps. But we will be watching you…

Shuttle moves round in a circle of thirteen
And we sound our rattles and we beat our drums
We're moving slow on the cold sand
Shuttle moves round in a circle of thirteen
We sing of your deep heart, we sing of your sad eyes
Shuttle moves round in a circle of thirteen
We will dance 'til our spirits bleed
We will dance 'til our spirits bleed
Shuttle moves round in a circle of thirteen
Mbaba Mwana, Waresa Songi ye ye
Shuttle moves round in a circle of thirteen
Become the rhythm of the Old Song
Become the rhythm of the Old Song
Shuttle moves round in a circle of thirteen
Makakēshé wakiva momo, makakēshé wakiva momo
Shuttle moves round in a circle of thirteen
Who will meet the witch queens as we sweep the snow clean?
Shuttle moves round in a circle of thirteen
We shall eat from you, we shall drink of you
Shuttle moves round in a circle of thirteen
Hegatty Pegatty lives on the moor,
Hegatty Pegatty open your door!
Shuttle moves round in a circle of thirteen
We ride the white flame unbounded
Shuttle moves round in a circle of thirteen
And we move within a spring coiled,
And we light the fires of many
Shuttle moves round in a circle of thirteen
Big laughing death women
Shuttle moves round in the House of the Weavers
Shuttle moves round in the House of the Weavers
Shuttle moves round in the House of the Weavers.

HEARTHSTONE SONG

Songs of the Forgotten People

We are come to this place from the wildwood shades
We are come from the hidden valleys
We have heard you call through the mist and the rain
We have felt your breath on the breeze
We have felt your breath on the breeze.

We have walked many days to the rhythm of your heart
Like an echo of drum on stone
These voices are woven with the threads of your song
These people are returning home
These people are returning home.

We will build our dwelling from the bones of the earth
We are wed to the body of the earth
We will draw our water from the rise of the stream
We are wed to the flow of the stream
We are wed to the flow of the stream.

We will kindle our fire from the heart of the wood
We will open our feathers on the wind
We receive our living from the soil and the chase
We are wed to the soul of the land
We are wed to the soul of the land.

Now the clans are gathered, the first prayer sung
The first hearth set on the ground
Our promise made, our union spun
To the spirit of this place we are bound
To the spirit of this place we are bound.

The buzzard is risen, the deer is at bay
The wolf is returned to her lair
We embrace you close on the cold of the earth
We touch you soft in the air
We touch you soft in the air.

We will dance many days to the rhythm of your heart
Like an echo of drum on stone
Our voices are woven with the threads of your song
To the spirit of this land we are bound
To the spirit of this land we are bound.

HEGATTY PEGATTY

A Circle of Thirteen

Hegatty Pegatty lives alone. Her house crouches low against the barren hill like a withered mushroom and the smoke from her fire twists and curls in solitude up through the vast and lonely sky. Hegatty Pegatty looks out from her small window and sees the empty valley. Hegatty Pegatty passes at dark along her track and hers are the only footfalls that echo in the night. Hegatty Pegatty likes to live alone. The stillness dreamily caresses her thoughts. The silence stoutly feeds her soul. Hegatty Pegatty's world is infinite and minute. Hegatty Pegatty travels far and deep and high, and she moves not a step from her hearthside. Hegatty Pegatty walks a rich and ragged road.

Hegatty Pegatty is a witch. Of course she is. She answers to no one. As she chooses she takes a cup of tea, grows hairs upon her chin and sleeps through the afternoon. As she chooses she talks to herself, observes the unseen and does the unexpected. As she chooses she lives the impossible dream, reinvents reality and tangos with time. Hegatty Pegatty cannot be tamed or tied or trapped. Her spirit is swift-footed and canny, and her walls are built of impenetrable courage. Roof of resolve and door of determination. No one can touch she who is a castle unto herself.

Hegatty Pegatty walks inside a coat. It is made up of other people's eyes and what they want to see. Outside the coat Hegatty Pegatty does her bit: *mad Hegatty, bad Hegatty, eater of children and spoiler of milk! Hairy Hegatty, stinky Pegatty, where is she going alone, alone?* But inside the coat she is walking strong and straight and clear, light of heart and bright of mind…

Hegatty Pegatty lives on the moor
Hegatty Pegatty open your door!
Huccaby Ruccaby Hagetty Tor
Catorby Ratorby Batorby Tor!

HERON FLY YOU HOME

Old Silverhead

A Last Blessing song offered when someone is preparing to die, this is sung to help them meet death with dignity and embrace it without fear, as well as to free the spirit from the body. It can also be sung whenever a circle of people prepare to go their separate ways; to bless their individual paths and wish them well on their journeys.

Buzzard call you back to the wild land
Heron fly you home
Journey to the soul of your own land
Where the Mothers wait for your return
Heron fly you home.

HERON VALLEY

Heron Valley

There's a maiden coming in
moving down through Heron Valley
see the maiden coming in
wearing spring in her hair.

Silver by the pool
naked in the clear air
tall against the birch
dancer on the damp earth.

She's the catcher of the breeze
she's the lover of the pale sun
she's the footstep on the moss
she's the laughter of the quick stream.

Silver by the pool
naked in the clear air
tall against the birch
dancer on the damp earth.

Beneath the lace of winter wood
she throws out her arms and she sings
calling birds behind her
that bring summer on their wings.

Silver by the pool
naked in the clear air
tall against the birch
dancer on the damp earth.

Through soft shades and glistening haze
swift she trails her gown of green
her sweet kiss, the rising sap
and her warm hand awakening

Silver by the pool
naked in the clear air
tall against the birch
dancer on the damp earth.

There's a maiden coming in
moving down through Heron Valley
see the maiden coming in
wearing spring in her hair.

Taste the yellow,
smell the new
touch the spring
feel the wood...

HOLLY WOMAN

Heron Valley

She is the eye of the storm
She is the centre of the wheel
She is the ever constant heart
She is the flame that burns still
And the year turns through yet she remains
Holly Woman unmoving, Holly Woman unchanged.

Fierce guardian of the winter storming
Silent watcher from the edge
Ancient memory and wisdom stories
Held in the seeds of her blood red
And the year turns through yet she remains
Holly Woman unmoving, Holly Woman unchanged.

So she sits amid the spring greening
The ripening gold will not touch her face
For she will be tomorrow
As she is today
And the year turns through yet she remains
Holly Woman unmoving, Holly Woman unchanged.

So we learn to greet our life changes
As we follow ebb and flow
Yet there is a place at our centre
Where the winds do not blow
And the year turns through yet we remain
Holy Women unmoving, Holy Women unchanged.

I come to you from the House of the Weavers
Houses of the Weavers
I come to you from the House of the Weavers
House of the Weavers
Dreaming grandmothers with wisdom hands and lizard tongue
Dreaming grandmothers with wisdom hands and lizard tongue.

I fly with you from the House of the Weavers
House of the Weavers
I fly with you from the House of the Weavers
House of the Weavers
Fly, fly with my eagle eye and willow wing
Fly, fly with my eagle eye and willow wing.

I dance with you in the House of the Weavers
House of the Weavers
I dance with you in the House of the Weavers
House of the Weavers
I step the weft, I walk the warp, I dance the spiral round
I step the weft, I walk the warp, I dance the spiral round.

I stand with you by the House of the Weavers
House of the Weavers
I stand with you by the House of the Weavers
House of the Weavers
Watch from the ridge, it is the bridge into another realm
Watch from the ridge, it is the bridge into another realm.

I now return into the House of the Weavers
House of the Weavers
I now return into the House of the Weavers
House of the Weavers
The veil lifted, the journey ended and now begun
The veil lifted, the journey ended and now begun

I come to you from the House of the Weavers
Houses of the Weavers
I come to you from the House of the Weavers
House of the Weavers

I am the stream and the cup that is filled
I am the bleeding and I am the blood
I am the woman who cries on the rock
I am the child who grows wise in the sun
I am the moon as she rises to full
I am the sister who comes from the south
I am the dance of the babe in the womb
I am the Spirit who breathes on the land
I am the Spirit who breathes on the land.

ICE

Weathered Edge paintings

She is ICE the Hunter
who prowls the frost bound slopes
armed with a delicately potent
dart of frozen fire.
She is the balance between
cruelty of diamonds and
the human warmth
of bones.
Her dance is a chase,
a raw pursuit,
an exquisite challenge.
She dances where
the fire is kindled
that unlocks the land,
that promises something
real and new,
poised inside
the belly of the year
at this time of
QUICKENING.

IN MY SISTERS' COUNTRY

Old Silverhead

I give you my copper
the blood of the soil
blood of me

You give me your amber
the tears of a tree
crying tree

The sun's kiss is deep and
it's sweet in my
sisters' country

The colours are bright
and we're tasting a
different beauty

Ul-lala ul-lala ul-lala ul-ley
Ul-lala ul-lala ul-lala ul-ley
Ul-lala ul-lala ul-lala ul-ley
Ul-lala ul-lala ul-lala ul-ley

The sun's kiss is deep and
it's sweet in my sisters' country
The sun's kiss is deep and
it's sweet in my sisters' country…

JAGUAR

House of the Weavers

She is a fiery raw goddess
With a blood red eye
In her womb she holds the universe
The earth clasped between her thighs
Her serpent power is rising
Her jaguar teeth are sharp
The wild beast is drumming
In her jungle heart
The wild beast is drumming
In her jungle heart

KNITTING SONG

Old Silverhead

Mother Grey making song within earth
Mother Grey mending life within earth
Mother Grey casting love within earth
Mother Grey knitting soul within earth

She's a witch who's stepping lightly
Newly croned within the land
And her hands are moving wisely
As she draws her magic down

Mother Grey making song within earth
Mother Grey mending life within earth
Mother Grey casting love within earth
Mother Grey knitting soul within earth

Dear love on your night journey
The dark has filled your sweet body
The forest heart has drawn you close
Far from the bright edges of morning.

Dear love on your night journey
The dark has filled your sweet body
You are lost from my embrace
And bitter the taste of my yearning.

Dear love on your night journey
The dark has filled your sweet body
And many cold winters shall pass
'Til we share again our returning.

Dear love on your night journey
The dark has filled your sweet body
I place you in your cold earth home
And I see your bird spirit soaring.

Dear love on your night journey
The dark has filled your sweet body
You drift beyond your lover's land
But I'll sing you back at our dawning.

LAU HĒ DUHTAN

Songs of the Forgotten People

A chant to honour the spirit worlds and the paths of magic, prayer and shamanic dream. Sung as a ritual trance. Translated meaning:
O weavers on this earth loom, I feel your hands at my threads
and this cloth it is our shared lives and the place at which we meet.

O veesood na'nat ud lekki ud lekki ud lekki....HWAY!
agahatseem pōro kuchan ro kuchan ro kuchan....HWAY!
neelalgusparg mi hway bōchi hway bōchi hway bōchi...HWAY!
raba nachilla hē duhtan hē duhtan hē duhtan...HWAY!

LAU HĒ KEHPĒ

Songs of the Forgotten People

This chant builds into a full-voiced celebratory dance. It honours the spirit of the wild and open land, and our feelings of homecoming, belonging and return.
Translation: *we are returning along the trail of the heron*

Lau hē lau hē
Lau hē kehpē lau hē kehpē
Lau he hē kerek-tak he hē
Lau hē ya kehpē lau hē ya kehpē

Spirit of old rock
Spirit of earth
You are beauty
You are life

A song for the spirit of home and hearthfire.

This fire is dancing
this child is laughing
this home is singing
lau hē raumi.

Cutting the summer reeds
stringing the willow bow
shaping the wet clay for
lau hē raumi.

Green herb is gathered
ripe berry is drying
herd pipe is calling
lau hē raumi.

Oiling the winter skins
twisting the strong fleece
travelling the carved wood to
lau hē raumi.

Cutting the summer reeds
stringing the willow bow
this home is singing
lau hē raumi.

LITTLE BIRD

Heron Valley

Little bird on your maiden flight
Tiny goddess that sits in my palm
Earth daughter with a daffodil smile
Girl child growing your tiny womb
My little woman, my little woman

Small sister with a big song
Sleepy friend with your dream-deep eyes
Spring flower blossoming brave and wild
Rosy angel riding with the stars
My little woman, my little woman

I am weaving the darkness
the black murmur of night
I am binding these shadows
within my tight cloth
And my fingers are plucking
at the rim of the world
And my oak wechi is pushing
at the frayed edge of time
I weave my hidden people
I weave my lost clans
I weave my hidden people
I weave my lost clans.

They run into the threads
and spread like tongues of fire
across the loom
And memory is caught fast
in the warp string
So the loom is drawing in
from old bones and from new seed
And the weaving is a net
to hold this moment
I weave my hidden people
I weave my lost clans
I weave my hidden people
I weave my lost clans.

Another weaver is calling
through the shifting veils
as the cloth is revealed
as the cloth is revealed.

So you shall have woven my time
as I am weaving yours
So you will be weaving my time
when my cloth has long since
faded to the earth
I have glimpsed you
through my dancing strings
And I hold a single strand
pulled from your weaving song.
I feel your hands around mine
as the cloth is slowly formed
as the cloth is slowly formed.

O weavers on this earth loom
I feel your hands at my threads
And this cloth it is our shared lives
and the place at which we meet

*wechi: heavy wooden loom comb for beating down the weft
threads*

Magdalene Magdalene
Etz Hayyim Hi
Magdalene Magdalene
Mayyim Hayyim Hi

Etz Hayyim Hi
Etz Hayyim Hi
Mayyim Hayyim Hi

She is the House
The House of the Soul
Etz Hayyim Hi

She is the Well
The Well of the Heart
She is the Tree of Life

Etz Hayyim Hi
Etz Hayyim Hi
Mayyim Hayyim Hi

Etz Hayyim Hi: *She is the Tree of Life*
Mayyim Hayyim Hi: *She is the Water of Life (Hebrew)*

MARE

The Oracle of Nights

She rode down hard upon us through
the silver spray, racing from
dark cliffs that rose along the water line,
we heard her panting breath
and thundering hoof, then the rich smell
of sweaty flanks, woman's and mare's,
reached us before she arrived,
with powerful staying of the beast
she drew level, every muscle
tensed and braced as she leaned low
into the wind,
her skin, alive and vibrant, caught
within the silver flood of light
that was the moon at full,
she circled us three times or more
huge thighs clenched around the creature,
broad back arched, nostrils flared,
a woman with a giant's might,
both challenger and honourable foe,
she flung back her head and raised a cry,
a waking call to each of us,
ride with me, she roared,
be untamed and magnificent,
summon strength into your body and your soul,
snatch up your boundaries, smash them hard
onto the crags, be freed,
then she turned the mare abruptly,
was soon racing out towards the sea,
leaping surf along the trailing light,
see how the moon is strong, she cried,
as moon's women so are we, as moon's women so are we.

Weathered Edge

I'm a storm in a bucket, a hot flash in the pan
I'm at sixes and sevens once more
In a bother, a pickle, a ruction, a tangle
A GREAT SEETHING VOLCANIC ROAR!
I feel volatile, irrational and really rather strange
I break a lot of dishes and I shout
Although I might seem normal inside I'm quite deranged
What are these raw feelings all about?

Inside each older woman lives a furnace **(furnace)**
A fire **(fire)** who knows where it will lead?
Don't worry if you burn, it's simply just your turn
For a touch of menopausal anarchy **(anarchy)**!
Inside each older woman dwells a chaos **(chaos)**
A chasm **(chasm)** who knows what it all means?
It can't get any worse so no matter if it bursts
Into a touch of menopausal anarchy **(anarchy)**!

I've endeavoured to keep calm and not to make a fuss
Bring disorder nor cause a commotion
But here's a little secret and it's just between us
THERE'S NO WAY TO STEM THIS WILD EMOTION!
I cannot be silent even when I should
Hell! I must speak my mind, I've had enough!
Restraint and diplomacy are all well and good but
For a woman in her middle years they're tough!

Inside each older woman spins a turmoil **(turmoil)**
A tempest **(tempest)** how scary can that be?
You really should be warned there's no proof against the storm
Of a touch of menopausal anarchy **(anarchy)**!
Inside each older woman there's a riot **(riot)**
A rampage **(rampage)** hormonal trickery
I hope you'll understand when we're getting out of hand
It's a touch of menopausal anarchy **(anarchy)**!
I hope you'll understand when we're getting out of hand
It's a touch of menopausal anarchy!

A cycle of songs and chants to acknowledge the shifts of life and perception that accompany the approach of menopause and middle age. It forms part of a ritual dance for midwomen, opening them to the possibilities of powerful change. Ma Ki-ay is an invocation to the ancient Mother of Time.

A crone has gently stroked my face
O Ma O Ma O Ma ki-ay
Her claw runs lightly through my hair
O Ma O Ma O Ma ki-ay
She whispers from a hidden place
O Ma O Ma O Ma ki-ay
She waves to me at the edge of my eye
O Ma O Ma O Ma ki-ay
As a stream my blood is changing course
O Ma O Ma O Ma ki-ay
My body is finding a different pulse
O Ma O Ma O Ma ki-ay
There is a bridge that I must cross
O Ma O Ma O Ma ki-ay
O Mother of time walk with me now
O Ma O Ma O Ma ki-ay

My maid stands far behind my back
O Ma O Ma O Ma ki-ay
Maid and crone at each end of the line
O Ma O Ma O Ma ki-ay
They sing in strange and lovely tones
O Ma O Ma O Ma ki-ay
They sing my bridge as I wait to pass
O Ma O Ma O Ma ki-ay
I see myself coming the other way
O Ma O Ma O Ma ki-ay

I reach myself coming the other way
O Ma O Ma O Ma ki-ay
There is a bridge that I must cross
O Ma O Ma O Ma ki-ay
O Mother of time walk with me now
O Ma O Ma O Ma ki-ay

MEET THE MIRROR, MELT AND MERGE THERE
TILT THE MIRROR, TIP THE TIME LINE
MIND THE MIRROR, MIND YOU MARK TIME
MID LINE, IT'S YOUR TIME TO TURN TIME

Midwoman is turning time   *O Ma O Ma O Ma ki-ay*
She draws the ends into a loop   *O Ma O Ma O Ma ki-ay*
Within her ageing sits her youth   *O Ma O Ma O Ma ki-ay*
Maid and crone walk hand in hand   *O Ma O Ma O Ma ki-ay*
Midwoman is turning time   *O Ma O Ma O Ma ki-ay*
Midwoman is turning time   *O Ma O Ma O Ma ki-ay*

Midwoman stands on a bridge   *O Ma O Ma O Ma ki-ay*
She wanders in a dangerous place   *O Ma O Ma O Ma ki-ay*
But she wears a map upon her face *O Ma O Ma O Ma ki-ay*
She carves her life into her skin *O Ma O Ma O Ma ki-ay*
Midwoman is turning time   *O Ma O Ma O Ma ki-ay*
Midwoman is turning time   *O Ma O Ma O Ma ki-ay*

Midwoman in her deep beauty   *O Ma O Ma O Ma ki-ay*
She's seen her power inside her eyes *O Ma O Ma O Ma ki-ay*
She's dancing backwards into time *O Ma O Ma O Ma ki-ay*
Maid and crone she carries both   *O Ma O Ma O Ma ki-ay*
Midwoman is turning time   *O Ma O Ma O Ma ki-ay*
Midwoman is turning time   *O Ma O Ma O Ma ki-ay*

She is MIST the Concealer
who guards the fragile opening
to the horned maze,
a puzzle and confusion
cast up by the ancient land.
She is everything we thought was lost
but which is only hidden.
Her dance is a threshold,
a strange test
drawn layer upon layer
over mind and eye.
She steps past
shifting lifetimes,
crosses into
veiled beginnings.
So she dances
down through dying shadows
and the half light of
GHOST EVE.

MOTHER OF THE MOOR

Heron Valley

Small river brings me to your gate
A sun-warmed place
Familiar smell of moss and leaves
You've always been the same.

Mother of the Moor you are
Mother of the Moor you are
Mother of the Moor you are
Mother of the Moor
And your body is stone and wood
And your heart is my hearth.

Breeze dances through me
And your fingers touch gently
This way, you say, listen close
And you will find me.

Mother of the Moor you are
Mother of the Moor you are
Mother of the Moor you are
Mother of the Moor
And your body is stone and wood
And your heart is my hearth.

Your daughter, she is my daughter
She's running through the fern
Your lover, he is my lover
He's reaching to the sun.

Mother of the Moor you are
Mother of the Moor you are
Mother of the Moor you are
Mother of the Moor
And your body is stone and wood
And your heart is my hearth.

My hearthstone rests in your lap
And I step softly
I come now to kindle your fire
And draw your water to me

Mother of the Moor you are
Mother of the Moor you are
Mother of the Moor you are
Mother of the Moor
And your body is stone and wood
And your heart is my hearth.

MOTH WING WOMAN

Grandmother Turtle

Moth Wing flies
through holes in the sky
behind which the Big Fire is burning.
Moth Wing soars
she spins as she's caught
in the sweet hot air high drifting.

Moth Wing curls
she arches and rolls
through the old star gate gently swinging.
Moth Wing eyes
see far on the rise
she rides the white flame unbounded.

Moth Wing Woman
I root my earth damp feet
and reach up to my night cloud hair.
Moth Wing Woman
I stand firm on this land
but I dance in the cool star bright air.

Moth Wing lips
brushed with the swift
soft kiss of her hidden mercy.
Moth Wing love
her silent call to flight
a feather on the wing of freedom.

Moth Wing heart
a smile in the dark
the joy of an endless wonder.
Moth Wing soul
light shadow in the black
a whisper through a timeless journey.

Moth Wing Woman
I root my earth damp feet
and reach up to my night cloud hair.
Moth Wing Woman
I stand firm on this land
but I dance in the cool star bright air.

MUDHEAD CLOWNS

Riven Inside

Written with respect for the wide deserts of California and Arizona.

Coyote Coyote Coyote you call we come!
Coyote Coyote Coyote you call we come!

Warriors dancing in long rows that bend like a reed
Even a battle must wait for the blessing of fools
Mix butterfly wings with the dust of a footstep
Here come the Mudhead Clowns
Here come the Mudhead Clowns

Arriving from nowhere and passing then into beyond
Sweet stink of the desert and rough as a rock that is torn
Life is the beat they are drumming too loudly
Here come the Mudhead Clowns
Here come the Mudhead Clowns

The fear is of wandering lost in a canyon of dreams
Courage is gathered like sweat on the breast and the thigh
Far stronger the truth of a warrior humbled
Here come the Mudhead Clowns
Here come the Mudhead Clowns

Water is spilt from the jars that we smash in the dirt
Our passion is fierce and we rub at our faces with earth
We sigh at the edge of a trance that is fading
Where are the Mudhead Clowns?
Here are the Mudhead Clowns
Where are the Mudhead Clowns?
Here come the Mudhead Clowns.

The wild in our loins is too strong to contain us
We eat at the walls like a dog that is tied
Cast down the beans to the feet of the Stamper
Cast down the corn to be scattered and spoiled

Coyote Coyote Coyote you call we come!
Coyote Coyote Coyote you call we come!

MYSTERY UNFOLDING

Heron Valley

Fox passing through the purple dusk
Calling buzzard lifts and plays the air
Bright mouse eye in the gorse
Brown trout journeys to source
There's a mystery unfolding
A mystery unfolding
There's a mystery unfolding
On the land.

Owl guardian dark wings of the night
Laughing otter spills into the stream
Small snake coiled in the grass
Heron moves across the marsh
There's a mystery unfolding
A mystery unfolding
There's a mystery unfolding
On the land.

NAMELESS DRUM

Weathered Edge

This song is for the people of the frozen lands and for all journeys north.

In these ancient northern lands, our shrine is the forest floor and our temple is the sky. Our own bodies are the altars on which we lay our offerings and prayers. Our rituals are spontaneous and direct communications with the land. Simplicity has always served us well in connecting us to the deep and ancient spirit of the landscape. And in these cold forests we make rhythm and sing. From the beginning we have created music, magic and prayer with bone and wood and horn and skin. Our drums are born from the raw fabric of the land, formed by our own hands from the gifts of nature. Our drum is the first and most simple expression of the many voices of the earth. It is the song of thunder, of rain and of stones, of wind and of water and of all the elements that move across the land. The drum is the belly bowl, the world, all of life. It is the heartbeat of the people, of the mother, of the child, of the very earth. The beat of the drum creates a web of sound that connects all parts to the whole. All the songs of the land are held within the sound of our drum. The drum is our wild vessel. It is our oracle, our hidden language and our spirit tongue. It is our shield and protection, a weapon as powerful as any blade. Anyone of us might enter through the gateway of the drum and ride there to the very edges of the world. The drum is the source of our revelation. It is a new and brilliant way to see.

The edge of the world is where I am bound
With a weapon of grace and a fine shield of sound
I can hear a familiar voice close at hand

The primordial song of a northern land
As it races the great sun over ancient snow
The drum beast is older than we can ever know
I've heard a journey north is a dangerous one
So ride hard through the skin of the nameless drum

How strong is the face of a woman's drum?
How far from the first rhythm have we come?
How solid the resonance of our beat?
How powerful the tread of our feet?   YA'KO!

Hey ya'ko Hey ya'ko nameless drum
Hey ya'ko Hey ya'ko sweet life drum
Hey ya'ko Hey ya'ko great world drum
Hey ya'ko Hey ya'ko this drum

NIGHT OF STAGS

Weathered Edge

A song for the early summer fertility festival (Beltane).

I will go
to where the fires are brightly fed
all through
the hidden Night of Stags.
I will carry
my secrets there
and I will shake
my heavy head.
They will scatter,
they will fly
like burning petals
from the tips
of my own horns.
My bare brow
is pale under the moon.
I will give my secrets generously
to you.

You will come
to where the waters are supped deep
all through
the dazzling Night of Stags.
You will feed me
with the life of plants,
a sacrament of green
upon my tongue,

and fold leaves
to channel rain
into my mouth
and you will sing
until the rain-soaked earth
absorbs
your silver song.
You will bring the living waters
to me.

I will go
to where the air is softly turned
all through
the crimson Night of Stags.
I will bring
my full and open bowl
brimming with
the budding year.
My breath
disturbs the surface of the bowl.
See how it shivers
and it stirs.
I will hold
this fertile vessel
as it wakes.
I will catch a thousand grains of light
for you.

You will go
to where the earth's a sacred bed
all through
the fragrant Night of Stags.
You will dance
a homage to the rain
and I will watch
the tapping of your toes.
Rivers roll
between the damp thighs
of the land.
Your dark hooves
are slipping on the soil.
We will dream
across the leaping fires.
You will guide the morning home
to me
all through the Night of Stags
all through the Night of Stags.

She is woman who sees
She is woman who sees
She is crone woman
Skull and bone woman
Moss and stone woman
Crone woman
Crone woman.

Deep earth cave mother
Dark moon blood mother
Blood mother
Blood mother.

She is woman who knows
She is woman who knows
She is hidden woman
She is shadow woman
Midnight cloak woman
Raven croak woman
Owl bat moth woman
Owl woman
Owl woman.

She is woman who waits
She is woman who waits

She is death mother
She is birth mother
Earth mother
Earth mother
Earth birth death mother.

She is night woman
Winter storm woman
Ancient hands woman
Wisdom woman
Old woman
Old woman.

She is woman who sees
She is woman who sees
She is night woman
She is night woman.

Old Silverhead, Old Silverhead
Here is a woman most impulsively led
Old Silverhead, Old Silverhead
It is the crowning glory of Old Silverhead

Slicing through reason with her quick-bladed mind
Crone illogical thinking keeps her happy and wise

Old Silverhead, Old Silverhead
Here is a woman most impulsively led
Old Silverhead, Old Silverhead
It is the crowning glory of Old Silverhead

Living with insight, she likes what she sees
Memory cut loose and wandering free

Old Silverhead, Old Silverhead
Here is a woman most impulsively led
Old Silverhead, Old Silverhead
It is the crowning glory of Old Silverhead

Caution dismantled, there's nothing to lose
To chase the unpredictable is what she will choose

Old Silverhead, Old Silverhead
Here is a woman most impulsively led
Old Silverhead, Old Silverhead
It is the crowning glory of Old Silverhead

OLD VALLEY

Songs of the Forgotten People

Ancient Dartmoor wedding song.

She came on the tide of the white moon sea
He rose like the sun from the Ancient Tree
And the memory's long of the Stone Woman
The root runs deep in the Green Woodsman.

They met on the edge where the wind passed by
They touched on the rise of a buzzard's cry
And the memory's long of the Stone Woman
The root runs deep in the Green Woodsman.

Song of the rock and heart of the tree
We'll walk together in the Old Valley.

She said,
The journey's long but the heart is true
I've blessed every step on the path to you
And the memory's long of the Stone Woman
The root runs deep in the Green Woodsman.

He said,
I've waited and watched where the shadows hung
I knew for a thousand years you would come
And the memory's long of the Stone Woman
The root runs deep in the Green Woodsman.

Song of the rock and heart of the tree
We'll walk together in the Old Valley.

So they sealed their pact on the highest tor
They cast their vows to the wide-open moor
And the memory's long of the Stone Woman
The root runs deep in the Green Woodsman.

Song of the rock and heart of the tree
We'll walk together in the Old Valley.

A tor is a high bare granite outcrop that can be found all over Dartmoor.

OLD WOMAN SLEEPS GOOD

Grandmother Turtle

Old Woman sleeps good
sleeps good on the land
becomes the red rock
becomes the white gum
becomes the desert sand
becomes the slow pulse
of the living earth
becomes the rhythm of the Old Song.

Old Woman walks good
walks good on the land
she carries no words
into the silence
of the wide plain
breathes in the deep fire
absorbs the long rains
her body molded
by the hard grains of the dry sand.

Old Woman sits good
sits good on the land
this no-words woman
awakes the serpent
gathers the red dust
gathers the desert sand
her basket heavy
with the life blood of the Big Dream.

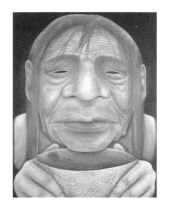

Old Woman walks good
walks good on the land
becomes the red rock
becomes the desert sand.

See through the mist where a doorway beckons
Where the half-light gathers and the dark veils fall
What we thought was lost is only hidden
From the dying shadows there's a distant call…

On Ghost Eve
Hex and hag and crone and spell
Bless this cauldron and stir it well
On Ghost Eve
On Ghost Eve

We've burned in fire but now we're cooling
We've drowned in waters but now we swim
We've run from the hounds but now we face them
The past was cruel but we didn't give in
The circle was scattered but we're still spinning
The cloth was torn but we'll weave it anew
The wine is spicy, the cup is brimming
And this night is proof that we made it through

On Ghost Eve
Hex and hag and crone and spell
Bless this cauldron and stir it well
On Ghost Eve
On Ghost Eve

Come with a wit that is brightly wicked
Come with a tongue that can cut through stone
Come with a will that is tough as granite
Come with the truth that you feel in your bones

Come with a cackle and a free-born spirit
Come with an edge that is sharp and new
Come with your depth and your ageless wisdom
Come with a cake and a warming brew.

On Ghost Eve
Hex and hag and crone and spell
Bless this cauldron and stir it well
On Ghost Eve
On Ghost Eve

We're the smoke from flames that keep on dancing
The difference that blows through a silent crowd
We're the love in a heart that has never stumbled
The dust on a rich and ragged road
We're the blessing of the woods and a curse on iron
The passion of moon and the wrath of sun
We're the bind and the cast and the whole damn magic
We have asked for it all and we'll answer to none

On Ghost Eve
Hex and hag and crone and spell
Bless this cauldron and stir it well
On Ghost Eve
On Ghost Eve

To declare your belief in witches
You have only to put the kettle on
As a pot keeps warm on a single ember
So a lot can be hidden in a single song
On Ghost Eve
On Ghost Eve….

She is RAIN the Bestower
who nourishes the budding year
with secrets given generously
from her full and open bowl.
She is that which binds
fierce fury to sweet passion,
both the offer and the gift.
Flower petals dripping from
the ends of silver horns,
a single drop of fertile light
that falls to touch the earth.
Her dance is an orgasm,
dangerous intimacy and
the union of two.
All this she dances
in a place where
fires are fed and
waters taken deeply on the
NIGHT OF STAGS.

RISE OF THE CORN

House of the Weavers

I sing the ripening corn to you
I sing this pathway to you
that you may come where two hills meet
and I wait at water's edge.
I hear your heartbeat through the earth
sitting in my joy of you
sitting in my joy of you
wind brings your whisper.
I watch the horizon
and feel my blood's deep pulse
I sing the ripening corn to you
that you may come.

RISING DAWN

House of the Weavers

Angels of the rising dawn
crystal mountain soul
speaking light, speaking light
touching gold, touching gold.

Angels of the rising dawn
gentle morning star
reaching high, reaching high
moving far, moving far.

In forest heart the man of leaves is dancing
He is source of stream and seed of life begun
At the edge of dawn his lithe green limbs are moving
Elfin flutes play and he steps the mystery round.
Green lord, green lord, spring maiden dances with you
Green lord, green lord, spring maiden dances with you.

Through ripened corn the golden man approaches
He wears the sun, the oldest light, as a crown
His fertile magic staff he bears before him
The air is hot as he lays down upon the land.
Corn king, corn king, harvest queen lays with you
Corn king, corn king, harvest queen lays with you

On open moor the man of stone is waiting
Between the worlds he guards the twilight hour
Through his eyes the ancient knowledge passes
His feet drum the throbbing beat of earth's deep power.
Stone man, stone man, weaving woman waits for you
Stone man, stone man, weaving woman waits for you.

Free running stag is leaping from the darkness
The wild hunt he leads across the sky
He carries strong the heartbeats of the old ones
He marks the trail into the deep and hidden ways
Horned god, horned god, moon goddess rises with you
Horned god, horned god, moon goddess rises with you

SEA WITCH

Weathered Edge

A Sea Witch swims where the surf unfolds
A Sand King lies on his bed of gold
She stares at him from the ocean's reach
And he watches her from a sun-kissed beach
As the waves are drawn to the sand
As the grains are held by the sea.

The Sea Witch raises her arms and lifts
Her voice to open the water's gift
She dances a life that is wild and strong
She sings a love that is ancient and long
And the Sand King leaps for her trailing song
Where the waves are drawn to the sand
Where the grains are held by the sea.

The Sand King takes up his bowl of shell
Strung with cords wound tight by a hidden spell
And the music he plays pours clear and white
Like a sunburst over the beach so bright
And the Sea Witch laughs in the dazzling light
And the waves are drawn to the sand
And the grains are held by the sea.

They climb high onto a rock, and roll
By the surf of light and the beach of gold
For a year and a day so they give their pledge
To meet and play on this glistening ledge
They have found their place by the water's edge
Where the waves are drawn to the sand
Where the grains are held by the sea.

House of the Weavers

I am a secret stream
I am running beneath the surface of the earth.
You are my constant dream
and you're running with me
beneath the surface of the earth.

I am a willow tree
I am growing on the surface of the earth.
You are a summer breeze
and you're blowing on
the surface of the earth.

I am an autumn leaf
I am lying on the surface of the earth.
You are those dancing feet
and you're dancing on
the surface of the earth.

I am a secret stream
I am a willow tree
I am an autumn leaf.

You are my constant dream
You are my summer breeze
You are my dancing feet
You are my dancing feet.

SHAMAN-CA

Grandmother Turtle

With my bird bone rattle and my goat skin drum
Shaman-Ca Shaman-Ca
With my cold river eye and my hot fire tongue
Shaman-Ca Shaman-Ca
Worlds spin fast when I stamp my feet
Body moves to an ancient beat
I will dance 'til my spirit bleeds
I will dance 'til my spirit bleeds
Shaman-Ca Shaman-Ca

I'm an unnamed star, I'm a ragged queen
Shaman-Ca Shaman-Ca
I'm an untamed womb, I'm a jagged seam
Shaman-Ca Shaman-Ca
Old goblin woman sits on the ledge
And the fire and the fury and the fear are wed
We croon and sway at the misty edge
We croon and sway at the misty edge
Shaman-Ca Shaman-Ca

Ca…ancient spinster!
Ca…faerie dancer!
Ca…totem rider!
Ca…soul entrancer!

My home is the claw of a tangled path
Shaman-Ca Shaman-Ca
A nest that rocks in a shifting marsh
Shaman-Ca Shaman-Ca
Do you see me when you're riding wild?
There's much to be learned through a crazy eye
Will you bring to me your madness child?
Will you bring to me your madness child?
Shaman-Ca Shaman-Ca

With my bird bone rattle and my goat skin drum
With my cold river eye and my hot fire tongue
I'm an unnamed star, I'm a ragged queen
I'm an untamed womb, I'm a jagged seam
You know that nothing is as it seems
You know that nothing is as it seems
Shaman-Ca Shaman-Ca
Shaman-Ca Shaman-Ca

SHE CUTS ICE

Grandmother Turtle

Amber-toothed wolf waiting
Raven eye close watching
North woman far-seeing
Knife in crisp air singing
Blade of ice cut cutting
Beak and claw flesh ripping
Blood on lips sip sipping
Spark from death releasing

Northern snows grip tightly
Bared-tooth winds pierce coldly
Frozen rocks rise darkly
Long nights bind land closely
Knife on stone grates harshly
Tooth on bone cracks sharply
Blood on snow spills brightly
Soul on ice moves lightly

Who will be the carrion
Who will feel the cold blade
Who will meet the witch queen
As I sweep the snow clean?

The doorway is narrow
and the walls push close about her.

I am the flower of the field:
as the lily among thorns so is my love among the daughters.

Heavy robes hang solid.
Weary body bound tight.

I sat down under his shadow whom I desired:
and his fruit was sweet to my palate.

She is held hard to the earth.

Thy lips, my spouse, are as a dropping honeycomb:
honey and milk are under thy tongue.

She stoops low to peer through a window,
very small.

The voice of my beloved knocking:
open to me, my sister, my love.
My soul melted when he spoke.

Warm sun touches cold stone.

I arose to open to my beloved:
my hands dropped with myrrh.
Behold he cometh leaping upon the mountains.

And joy flies out on the wings of a thousand butterflies.

The fig tree hath put forth her green figs,
the vines in flower yield their sweet smell.

A heart unbound.
A spirit risen high.
A horizon spread wide.

I will go up into the palm tree
and will take hold of the fruit thereof.

She is balanced in a moment of perfection.

Flee away o my beloved and be like to the roe
and to the young hart upon the mountain.

The ecstasy of one renounced.
The passion of a sister.

Italicized words from Solomon's Canticle of Canticles.

She is SNOW the Protector
and she has walked
the long hoop
through the curving trail
of many thousand years.
She is that which is held safe
within the trap.
Young eyes watch through
old year's face hung loose
across her own
and the blood of age
melts slowly.
Her dance is a return,
a doorway again entered,
a loop made out of time.
She dances at a still point,
life inside of death,
gold beneath cold black,
motionless beside
the silent breath of
MIDWINTER.

SONGI NIGHT HIDDEN

Grandmother Turtle

She is the dance
The secret fire
Deep running pool
Of this desire
She holds the night
Between her thighs
She rocks the moon
Across the sky
And eats the stars
She eats the stars
She eats the stars.

Mbaba Mwana
Waresa Songi ye ye
Mbaba Mwana
Waresa Songi ye ye

She rises through
The sighing reeds
A midnight prayer
A whispered dream
Caressed within
Her silvered arms
This jewel hidden
In velvet palm
She eats the stars
She eats the stars
She eats the stars.

Mbaba Mwana
Waresa Songi ye ye
Mbaba Mwana
Waresa Songi ye ye

SONG OF THORN (a protection)

Weathered Edge

I walk an invisible path
I sing a silent song
I dance an untouchable dance
And nothing of my world is seen
And nothing of my world is heard
And nothing of my world is seen

I am secret thorn I am secret thorn
I am secret thorn I am secret thorn

I live an imaginary life
I dwell in a lost place
I climb to unreachable heights
And nothing of my world is seen
And nothing of my world is heard
And nothing of my world is seen

I am secret thorn I am secret thorn
I am secret thorn I am secret thorn

I long for the comfort of briar
I crave the kiss of thorns
The nettle's sting is my lover
And the sweet embrace of gorse

And nothing of your world is real to me
Nothing of your world is real...
YOU GET BACK FROM ME
I am secret thorn......

We met a woman on a journey
inwards to the illness that
her body had chosen to take,
we sat awhile and listened
as she told us of her travels,
not in words for she had none
and wore a veil about her face,
yet clearly she spoke through
every movement of her limbs,
her shaven head and eyebrows,
the tight bindings worn around her wrists,
and her hands constantly twisting
a line onto her wooden spool
behind which fell a fragile lace,
her fingers told us this: *if I should*
turn this thread until the end,
I'll find the point at which I may return
and I will have made a lace
so stunning in its beauty,
a web in which my cancer will be caught
so it becomes a flower in the pattern,
a shape within the whole design,
thus I will fetch it back
and create beauty with it,
we touched the woman briefly
and wished her well upon her journey and return,
and wished her well upon her journey and return.

SPINMOTHER

Old Silverhead

Giving birth a thousand times
Giving birth a thousand times
To be a mother of so much
To be a mother of so much
This life, I'm the spindle of this life
This life, I'm the spindle of this life

This life a complex pattern
I tangle it into one knot
This life an outrageous gift
This life a heady brew
This life so delicately coiled
In splendid folds around my hips

Giving birth a thousand times
Giving birth a thousand times
To be a mother of so much
To be a mother of so much
This life, I'm the spindle of this life
This life, I'm the spindle of this life

It moves so quickly, it moves so fast
It moves so quickly, it moves so fast
There will be stillness but not yet
There will be stillness but not yet
This life, I'm the spindle of this life
This life, I'm the spindle of this life

Giving birth a thousand times...

I am the spindle of my life
I am the spindle of my life
Here I go spinning inwards
Here I go spinning outwards
Here I go spinning without words
Here I go spinning without words

Giving birth a thousand times...

Meanwhile strands of life arrive
They are coming from all sides
Trailing past me in the mud
And I run to catch them up
And I plait the strands into my belt
And I plait the strands into my belt

Giving birth a thousand times
Giving birth a thousand times
To be a mother of so much
To be a mother of so much
This life, I'm the spindle of this life
This life, I'm the spindle of this life.

SPRING BLESSING

Riven Inside

We have heard the song of the quickening year
and the morning's invitation
In the belly of the green maid something stirs
in bright anticipation

Bring through the wakening seed!
Bring through the wakening seed!
We dance a rite to the old bride well
and around the twisted hazel
We dance a rite to the old bride well
and around the twisted hazel

STONECRONE

Old Silverhead

Stonecrone is a woman moving into the second phase of old age. She enters
into a relationship with the land that is ageless, profound and still. She
travels deep below soil and sand into timeless rock and stone.

Deep to this stone body
deep to this flint heart
deep to these granite limbs
deep to this rock belly
deep to this chalk flesh
deep to these jewelled veins

Scratch down my claws
scratch down my claws
deepening
deepening
and still.

She is STORM the Drummer,
untamed reckless bearer
of the drum named
Berry's Skin.
She is the place
where fearsome chaos
turns into a liberating
wilderness of soul.
Goat toe rattles roughly clatter.
Ochre powders crushed
to paint the power
driven to the ground.
Her dance is a reckoning,
the turning point for justice won.
A scorpionic anger,
raising madness to an art.
She dances where
the final chant is sung
and intense swells of energy
flow backwards at the
AUTUMN EBB.

STRANGE ENOUGH, DEEP ENOUGH

Riven Inside

I can weave you a basket
wound around with vines and withy
deep enough to hold the world
deep enough to hold the world
I can weave this for you
I can weave this for you

I can make you a rattle
carved and filled with river pebbles
loud enough to call a storm in
loud enough to call a storm in
I can make this for you
I can make this for you

I can bring you wine and honey
gathered from the summer meadow
sweet enough to catch a promise
sweet enough to catch a promise
I can bring this for you
I can bring this for you

I can stitch you a blanket
hemmed with fire and winter silence
wide enough to warm a lifetime
wide enough to warm a lifetime
I can stitch this for you
I can stitch this for you

I can grow you a forest
sown with lost and hidden places
strange enough to claim your dreams
strange enough to claim your dreams
I can grow this for you
I can grow this for you

I can paint you a memory
bound with mist and waiting faces
long enough to find an answer
long enough to find an answer
I can paint this for you
I can paint this for you

I can sing you a landscape
born of earth and stone and water
close enough to feel like home
close enough to feel like home
I can sing this for you
I can sing this for you

I can give you a story
tied with words of green and amber
strong enough to reach the end
strong enough to reach the end

SUMMER BLESSING

Riven Inside

Summer swings her broad hips
as we fell the sweet hay
with the slow petal drift
of the softening day
bold cast of the light
full turn of the sun
and a warmth that will linger
when summer is done

Oh merry down merry down merry down lay
fell the ripe hay merry down lay
down merry merry down merry down lay
fell the ripe hay merry down lay

Summer smiles as she plays
we taste salt on our skin
and bare feet are laid mid
rich measures of green
swift curve of the swallow
bright weave of the stream
and a warmth that will linger
where summer has been

Oh merry down merry down merry down lay
fell the ripe hay merry down lay
down merry merry down merry down lay
fell the ripe hay merry down lay

She is SUN the Destroyer
who has carefully placed
beneath her meadow apron
a scythe called
Harvest Kiss.
She is both the body burdened
and the body filled.
A sacrifice takes place
where long shadows reach
into the centre of the corn.
Her dance is a renewal,
cut down at peak to
make the plenty.
She has far greater
sacrificial gifts to bear.
She dances as her memories
enwrap the lazy hours,
warm amber, golden grasses,
and honey dipped with
heady mountain thyme,
rich culmination of the
HARVEST.

TESTIMONY

Weathered Edge

I fell asleep
in a precious land
and I awoke
to find the land had gone.
All that remained
was a torn strip
wound between my fingers,
a tattered fragment
even now being frayed
by a soft wind.
I could not remember
what it was to me.
I could not remember
what it was to me.

I smoothed flat
the piece of land
but I still could not see
where it belonged.
It was already unravelling
in my hands.
I concentrated hard
and as the fragment finally dissolved
I reached out and caught
A last remaining thread
I reached out and caught
a last remaining thread

Then I remembered
how this small strip
once fitted something
that I had lost
very long ago
very long ago
very long ago
very long ago

When the painting is complete
what is happening in the space
beyond its boundaries?
when the song is finished off
what can be heard as the last notes
fade away?….

THE BRIGHT EDGES OF MORNING

Songs of the Forgotten People

Small child on your night journey
The moon has filled your sweet body
The forest heart has drawn you close
Far from the bright edges of morning.

Small child on your night journey
The moon has filled your sweet body
You drift beyond your mother's land
But I'll sing you back at the dawning.

THE CARVED SCAVENGER

Riven Inside

One who is without courage
will be granted a refuge
where all is absolved
by the Writer of Vows
and compelled to journey
until the Carved Scavenger
shall be torn apart
shall be torn in two

THE CRAVEN
GIVEN HAVEN
AND SHRIVEN
BY SCRIVENER
AND DRIVEN
UNTIL GRAVEN RAVEN
IS RIVEN…

So she journeyed to sit at the ocean edge
and saw the sun move low against the sky.
The waves of her aloneness she wrapped about her
and her tears fell hot into the sea.
Then across the sand came the sun towards her,
and through her open eyes it stepped inside her.
And she understood that he who had been wandering long
at the edge of infinity was now close at hand.
And so she came back to her hearth
and waited in the fields and kept watch in the valley.
And she sang out the hymn of his returning.
From a distant star she saw him
and when at last he arrived their meeting was complete,
for through the parting had they become
each a piece of the other.
And from the point of greatest darkness
to the time of greatest light
did they unfold the edges of their story
and plant seeds into the ground.

And they lay within a huge white egg
and dreamed that the sun poured full upon the earth
and that the night held hidden blessings.
Then the rains came in abundance, the thunder rolled
and wings beat the air into a storm.
A great cedar burst from the soil
and rose with arms extended into the sky.
At last she went to the tree
and she opened her body
and gave birth to a small fish
which held the moon between its lips.

THE MASK

Heron Valley

The travellers spoke in this way:
we journeyed far through this country
and the bundles on our backs grew heavy
with experience
with experience.

And our eyes were dulled from seeing
the surfaces of many things
yes the surfaces of many things
but the hearts of few
but the hearts of few.

By a bridge sat a woman
no stranger yet strange she seemed
she wore the faces of all those we'd known
and had yet to meet
and had yet to meet.

The woman spoke: you search hard
but you do not have the eyes to find
I've made a mask through which to see
all sides of everything
all sides of everything.

We took the mask from her hands
and looking through we saw
the Woman in the Land
we saw the Spiral in the Stone
and the Singer in the Well
we saw the power in ourselves
we saw the power in ourselves.

Now we travel with new eyes
and to those who share our company
we give the mask through which to see
all sides of everything
all sides of everything.

THE MEAD BENCH

Riven Inside

A traditional pagan drinking song
remembered from the mead houses of old England!

Change is a door that is hanging wide open
A heathen's a soul that is lively and free
Love is a fruit that is ready and ripe
When you sit on the mead bench in warm company

THE OLDEST MAGIC

Weathered Edge

We come on a curve of light in the pale naked dawn
We come tattooed and painted with green serpent coils
We come in woven nettle and small bird wings
We come in wild ribbony rags and bright things
We know the oldest magic is tenderly held
We know the oldest magic is tenderly, tenderly,
tenderly held.

We are the barefoot runners with life beneath our feet
We are the vibrant seed within each new day we greet
We are impulsive freedom and a reckless energy
We are lit up with shimmering possibilities
We know the oldest magic is fearlessly held
We know the oldest magic is fearlessly, fearlessly,
fearlessly held.

We feel the stir of breezes that pull us from our dreams
We feel the urge that brings us to the sweet embracing stream
We feel the changes ripple to the edges of the land
We feel the sap rising through this ancient birthing ground
We know the oldest magic is quietly held
We know the oldest magic is quietly, quietly,
quietly held.

We are returned to this land, we are renewed
We kiss the earth awake as lovers do
We are the excited alchemy of the spring
We are the chaotic summoning of the wind
We know the oldest magic is wondrously held
We know the oldest magic is wondrously, wondrously,
wondrously held.

We are the barefoot runners with life beneath our feet
We are the vibrant seed within each new day we greet
We are impulsive freedom and a reckless energy
We are lit up with shimmering possibilities
We know the oldest magic is joyfully held
We know the oldest magic is joyfully, joyfully,
joyfully held.

THE RAGGED MEGS

Riven Inside

This song is performed as a ritual pagan dance, which in a later form was to become morris dancing. The dance is raw and earthy, and intended to raise the energy of the natural world. It ends in the chaotic disintegration of the last verse.

The Ragged Megs in a mazy dance
The Ragged Megs in a mazy dance
It's very strange, very strange…

Jagged and precious irregular pieces of LIFE!
Tattered and beautifully intricate moments of LIFE!
There's always a reason, there's always a season
There's always a reason, there's always a season to dance!

Dance at the edges remembering patterns of LAND!
Dance in the middle revealing the patterns of LAND!
There's always a reason, there's always a season
There's always a reason, there's always a season to dance!

Making things happen with every step of the DANCE!
Unwinding the magic with every turn of the DANCE!
There's always a reason, there's always a season
There's always a reason, there's always a season to dance!

Constant motion of earth and moon
Ancient power of water and soil
Enduring power of wind and fire
There's always a reason, there's always a season
There's always a reason, there's always a season to dance!

With tooth and bone
and twig and stone
and feather and bell
and mirror and shell
and hair and horn
and ash and thorn
and seed and shoot
and resin and root
There's always a reason, there's always a season
There's always a reason, there's always a season to dance!

Here is the hag with a fearsome claw
She'll catch you in her dribbling jaw
Black Annis will eat you!
Black Annis will get you!
RUN!

THE RIVEN STONE

Riven Inside

The melody for this song was adapted from the 16th century English ballad 'The Three Ravens'.

This song shall of a maiden tell *riven-ah riven-ay*
And of the man that she loved well *riven-ay*
They dwelt in lands of green and gold
Where myth was young and wisdom old
riven-ah riven-ah riven-ay

A pale minstrel came to that hall *riven-ah riven-ay*
His song enchanted the people *riven-ay*
He sang of men who'd gladly roam
When they are called to the Riven Stone
riven-ah riven-ah riven-ay

Her man was troubled from the start *riven-ah riven-ay*
The song enslaved his eager heart *riven-ay*
He was caught up within its dream
The maiden could not waken him
riven-ah riven-ah riven-ay

One night he stood at her window *riven-ah riven-ay*
Through tears he cried that he would go *riven-ay*
I must leave life and love and home
For I hear the call of the Riven Stone
riven-ah riven-ah riven-ay

He could not know, he ne'er looked back *riven-ah riven-ay*
That she ran stumbling in his track *riven-ay*
She journeyed hard for many days
While snow and ice about her lay
riven-ah riven-ah riven-ay

When her feet were worn to bone *riven-ah riven-ay*
Then she reached the Riven Stone *riven-ay*
There the trail left by her man
Into that stone was laid and gone
riven-ah riven-ah riven-ay

She made a dwelling sparse and cold *riven-ah riven-ay*
Close within the Stone's shadow *riven-ay*
Many long years she waited there
Believing he'd return to her
riven-ah riven-ah riven-ay

The maid became she poor and thin *riven-ah riven-ay*
The years were lines worn in her skin *riven-ay*
But one morning came out from the Stone
A man she knew to be her own
riven-ah riven-ah riven-ay

The young man laughed up to the sun *riven-ah riven-ay*
Old Hag, he cried, my quest is done *riven-ay*
And stand you not before me there
I ride to see my maiden fair
riven-ah riven-ah riven-ay

He rode away, he had no mind *riven-ah riven-ay*
Of the turns and twists of time *riven-ay*
Though she had waited forty year
But forty days had brought him here
riven-ah riven-ah riven-ay

She watched him go, what could she do *riven-ah riven-ay*
Then was her heart riven in two *riven-ay*
I've lost life and love and home
Because of the call of the Riven Stone
riven-ah riven-ah riven-ay

A rock it stands on common ground *riven-ah riven-ay*
'Tis smooth and chill beneath your hand *riven-ay*
Remember those that wait alone
Split in two by the Riven Stone
riven-ah riven-ah riven-ay

THE SISTERHOOD OF WEAVERS

Weathered Edge

A chant sung in many layers to honour ancient women of wisdom,
and their quiet and powerful work.

The Sisterhood of Weavers
The Sisterhood of Weavers
The threads we bind
The cloth we free
The threads we bind
The cloth we free

The Sisterhood of Weavers
The Sisterhood of Weavers
We bind
We free
We bind
We free

We are a sisterhood of many diverse and individual women, who
are somehow, amazingly, miraculously, connected by a common
bond, a shared understanding. Where do we find our oldest,
deepest, most enduring point of contact? We find it in the
knowing that each of us stands as part of a vast, ancient, sacred
circle of womankind. Nothing can unite us so strongly, so closely,
as this simple awareness and grateful appreciation of our
sisterhood. And in our humility we know to hold our vast power
gently. And in our simplicity we know how to make a difference
quietly…

THE SKIN MASK

Weathered Edge

She wears a delicate mask of skin
The face of Old Woman Gone
She walks in deep tracks still warm with blood
The steps of Old Woman Gone

Her holly shaft blade is kind and bright
As it slips into that which is passed
The silent snow gathers her fragile words
Softly whispered through her skin mask

Avo avo choley ki garam
Choley choley ba'way ma

She has travelled this loop many thousand years
The long trail of New Woman Come
She is poised at a fold in the cloth of time
The doorway of New Woman Come

Her holly beads harbour a hidden strength
That she carries hung safe at her waist
The silent snow brushes her waiting form
As she sings through the ancient skin face

Avo avo choley ki garam
Choley choley ba'way ma

Dancing the death
Dancing the life
And dancing all that returns ma

I survived
the ocean's wide hunger
the claw of bear
and the hook of man
river to sea
ocean to river
through turbulent waters
back to the wisdom of you
the wisdom of you.

If you chose not to love me
the mountains would crumble
the sky would stop breathing
and waters would darken
bereft of the light that is you
this is true.

I turn away
from the salt sea that pulled me
down through white waters
knowing how great was the distance to go
I swam at the edge
vast circles of motion
my timing was perfect
but now I am done
I long for the wisdom of you
the wisdom of you.

I leap
wildly at boulders
I think now of flying
so strong is the yearning
for a hill stream remembered
and desire for the wisdom of you
the wisdom of you.

Changer and changing
everything moving
I will travel a river returning
river to sea
ocean to river
back to intuitive springs
and the wisdom of you
the wisdom of you
the wisdom of you.

Beyond the early mists a long low dwelling sits close to the land, walls of stone and woven wicker, roof of reed thatch, through which smoke filters and then drifts away. A constant undulating murmur from inside, and a drum is sounding bass and slow. And there the door of twisted wood and ivy vine, a mare's skull hung bleached by the sun, and feathers from grey heron spinning in the breeze. The air is scented rich with pine resin and sweet herbs, and the door veil pulled aside to let the morning rays reach in to touch and warm the women sat within.

We squat in a circle on the earthen floor, around a ring of candle fire and sing. Our voices coil and slide above our heads as, eyes closed, we pray in the perfect beauty of the moment. This is the Women's House, and we the company of women who have gathered here to sing; to give ceremony, to celebrate a bridge across transition, to honour a growing and a change, another rite of passage on another woman's road. And placed upon our shrine, the many gifts that we have brought; clear water, rock and bundle; feather, bone and flower. And we call to O Ma Ki-ay, that constant Mother of Time, with whom we travel onwards through the spiral turns of life.

Rites of passage, initiations and celebrations serve to concentrate and give value to growth and changes in our lives, to give our journey different meanings, to offer us a vision of the whole. As women we mark the passing of time through transformations in our bodies, with the flow and ebb of bleeding, the shapeshifting of face and womb and breast and vulva that we experience as we age. We may travel in unfamiliar territories of mind and mood. And as we are aware of those who have walked this way before us, so we are also mindful of the younger women who follow on behind.

The Women's House exists inside the spirit of our gatherings, a place of the imagination and of the heart but as physical as we choose to make it. The Women's House is created by our circle, by our group voice, or by an individual woman who sits quietly alone. This is the house of our foremothers and of all the ancestor women and it is filled with their remembered voices, as ancient as the land.

The Women's House protects our common bonds as women and holds safe our universal prayers. Within the Women's House we share our rituals and rites of passage; we sing and chant and pray and dance and drum. We share the many experiences of our journeys through life; our wise thoughts and skills; our grieving, anger and delight. Within the Women's House we meet to build our visions, to map our journeys and to speak of our desires.

The Women's House is about having an awareness of ourselves standing in a long unbroken chain of women, connected to each other across barriers of time and place. It is about establishing our place within the community of women and a sisterhood that exists beyond the differences of land and culture. In the Women's House ancient women speak to us of the things that they have learned. New women come to embark on their adventure. Spirit women dwell inside our own skins and watch through our eyes. Forgotten women wait for us to remember them. This is the Women's House, and we the company of women who have gathered here to sing…

Where our foremothers have laid their ancient bones
We still have a clan to sing our story home

Where a trail has led us deep into the cave
We still have the night to urge us to be brave

Where river, stone and earth have touched us deep inside
We still have this land to call us to the wild

Where we travel on the long and plaited road
We still have our life to bind us to our goal

This is our clan
This is our night
This is our land
This is our life
This is our clan
This is our night
This is our land
This is our life

TOAD

Into the room we wandered
where the old old woman sat,
she squatted on the floor,
her thighs she pulled apart
and with her flat hand open
she slapped at her pudenda,
rhythmically she struck herself
the lips of her vagina crimson moist,
and still she slapped and chanted
her rhythm never slowing
her head thrown back, her throat stretched up
and so she called out to the power
that formed and swelled before her
as she slapped at her pudenda
to raise the crimson juices
of the power that was emerging,
as we stepped back from her
we saw that all around her
other very ancient women
were sat with legs pulled open
as they slapped and chanted
and the power was pouring freely
from their crimson-edged pudenda
from their crimson-edged pudenda.

House of the Weavers

Drum your footsteps to the sacred mountain
Lay down on the bleeding earth and sigh
Breathe the rhythm of the Mother sleeping
Listen to her dream, she whispers: Come alive!

Tread gently on the earth
Breathe gently of the air
Lie gently in the water
Touch gently to the fire

She bears the scars of our fears and follies
The dark night hovers and the world sits blind
But the waters flow and the moon is singing
Daughter winds are gathering and hope is high.

Tread gently on the earth
Breathe gently of the air
Lie gently in the water
Touch gently to the fire

You were born of her, she gave you being
She healed your body and brought your soul fire
When the Mother wakes we must awaken with her
We will fade away if we let her die.

Tread gently on the earth
Breathe gently of the air
Lie gently in the water
Touch gently to the fire
Tread gently on the earth

TURQUOISE LADY

House of the Weavers

Sweet Mother Ocean
Turquoise Lady
Deep fertile hidden waters
Blessed moon dance of the sea.

Strong Mother Ocean
Turquoise Lady
Mighty swell of lion roaring
Rising in your wild beauty.

Ancient Mother Ocean
Turquoise Lady
Whispering soft your secret dreaming
Rolling constant journey.

Sacred Mother Ocean
Turquoise Lady
Waiting shore and brooding rock
Washed by your waves of destiny.

TWILIGHT TONGUE

Weathered Edge

This chant is used to awaken a new drum and to bless future journeys through the rhythms of the drum. Twilight tongue refers to a hidden spirit language sung by ancient drummers.

Ror-ror y hāt
Mōōr y dān-a, mōōr y dān-a
Aya lufēyo, aya lufēyo
Heyi yāpa, heyi yāpa

Owl is come
Cries to people, cries to people
So we may see with, so we may see with
Brilliant eyes, brilliant eyes

TWO DRUMBEATS

Heron Valley

Through the softening night she's waiting
Listening close to distant whispers
As two hidden drums are measuring
A steady tread towards the dawn light
And the secrets of her dark womb
Are spilling out into the morning
And the cedar flute is playing
As the little one emerges.

Will you dance with me sweet daughter
Within the many circles of our lives
Held together by two drumbeats
Heart drum of the mother
Heart drum of the child.

Two women now are gathering
The harvest of their planting
As a bridge across the planet
Two belly bowls are beating
And the heart songs of the new ones
Are rising through the cloud drift
In the sky two stars are brightening
As they witness this beginning.

Will you dance with me sweet daughters
Within the many circles of our lives
Held together by two drumbeats
Heart drum of the mother
Heart drum of the child.

In the fire glow of the circle
Two drums are holding rhythm
And the ring of women dancing
New life into the dry land
Swaying in the shadows
Calling out into the black sky
Arm to shoulder slowly turning
In the swell born of their spinning.

Will you dance with me sweet daughters
Within the many circles of our lives
Held together by two drumbeats
Heart drum of the mother
Heart drum of the child.

To the high land they have journeyed
Words of truth and eyes of vision
A hundred thousand women
And a hundred thousand heartbeats
Pounds the deep drum of the Mother
Pulsing belly, surging power
Bearing down into the warm earth
At the birthing of this new time.

Will you dance with me sweet daughters
Within the many circles of our lives
Held together by two drumbeats
Heart drum of the mother
Heart drum of the child.

WALKING AS BEFORE

Songs of the Forgotten People

We have always been walking through this land.
We have always worn its vision like a skin,
but on the inside.
There has never been a time
when this river has not chilled our veins.
The track is strongly felt.
We are walking, we are walking as before
and our footsteps fit.
We pass that fragile moment
when everything becomes itself
but more so.
Look to each other across chasms of ancient time.
We are moving round a single unchanging point.
Move to the very edge
where the old world ends
and something else begins....

And we have always been walking through this land
And we have always worn its vision like a skin
The track is strongly felt, walking as before
And our footsteps fit, walking as before
Move to the very edge where the old world ends
And something else begins, something else begins
Move to the very edge where the old world ends
And something else begins, something else begins.

Your soul is flying to the weathered edge
These wings will guide you to the weathered edge
I too am yearning for the weathered edge
I'll find you waiting at the weathered edge

The edge is narrow
That we must balance on
But your heart is fierce
And your wings are broad and strong

Your soul is flying to the weathered edge
These wings will guide you to the weathered edge
I too am yearning for the weathered edge
I'll find you waiting at the weathered edge

You've travelled wisely
Your courage knew no bounds
You held your power gently
And you loved the life you found

Your soul is flying to the weathered edge
These wings will guide you to the weathered edge
I too am yearning for the weathered edge
I'll find you waiting at the weathered edge

This land is vast
That I will wander through
But every distant track
Will one day bring me home to you

Your soul is flying to the weathered edge
These wings will guide you to the weathered edge
I too am yearning for the weathered edge
I'll find you waiting at the weathered edge
My soul is flying to the weathered edge
These wings will guide me to the weathered edge…

WEDDING SONG

Songs of the Forgotten People

I have watched you swim where waters meet
I have listened to your secret name
I have breathed deeply into your dream
My drum has sung your journeys and your returns
I have lain your sleeping skins at my marriage fire
I have shed my good blood at my marriage door
I give you this clay bowl it is my earth belly
And this belt by which to wear my love
I have danced my heron for you
I have danced my heron for you.

I have watched you run on distant hills
I have seen your breasts painted with blue
I have tied my shadow to your heels
My pipes have sung your long flight and your nesting
I have hung your loom beneath my marriage roof
I have rubbed spring sap around my marriage door
I give you this bone knife it is my forest body
And this flute on which to play my heart
I have danced my buzzard for you
I have danced my buzzard for you.

WIND
Weathered Edge paintings

She is WIND the Summoner
who releases quick-fingered,
fast-flown seeds of change
from her precious
wellspring pod.
She is wild exhaustion
lightly transformed into
exhilarating joy.
Hare's egg nested under
a spell of twisted hazel.
Her dance is an awakening,
a great momentous birthing,
calling, urging new life out
onto the surface of the land.
She dances through
impulsive freedoms,
small bright leaves,
and the dynamic
early mornings of
SPRING RISE.

Riven Inside

A bare-armed tree above my head
The cold black earth beneath me
A northern wind to kiss my skin
A cloak of ice to sheath me

A promise from the deepest night
To hold me close and safely
A blessing to this winter light
That quietly burns within me

AFTERWORD

In the house of our mothers,
our many ancient mothers,
we are held by a truth
that is deep and strong.
From the drums of our bodies
we are sounding a rhythm,
it is powerful and raw,
it is the source of our very first song.
The bones of our limbs
play on the skins of our bellies
and this truth that we hear
is a simple one.
It is the heat of our tears
and the tremble of our hearts
as we return to the soft dark beat
of our beautiful
nameless drum.

A word of thanks to those who have in some way inspired the writing of these songs: my son Leaf Hillyer, my daughter Cedar Shaw, Guillermo Martinez, Robert Holdstock, Petra and Rupert, Jackie and Brian, Andrew Forrest, Naomi Ocean, Kiya Ocean, Ana Tonu, my mother Kate Hillyer…and, most specially, Nigel Shaw.